Spiral to Infinity Steve Allen

"Fractal images are often made up of small images-within-images, constantly repeating and going smaller and smaller."– **Steve Allen**

Investigations

IN NUMBER, DATA, AND SPACE®

Fish Lengths and Animal Jumps

Measurement   UNIT 5

Editorial offices: Glenview, Illinois • Parsippany, New Jersey • New York, New York
Sales offices: Boston, Massachusetts • Duluth, Georgia
Glenview, Illinois • Coppell, Texas • Sacramento, California • Mesa, Arizona

scottforesman.com

The Investigations curriculum was developed by TERC, Cambridge, MA.

T E R C

This material is based on work supported by the National Science Foundation ("NSF") under Grant No. ESI-0095450. Any opinions, findings, and conclusions or recommendations expressed in this material are those of the author(s) and do not necessarily reflect the views of the National Science Foundation.

ISBN: 0-328-23730-2

ISBN: 978-0-328-23730-2

6 7 8 9 10-V003-15 14 13 12 11 10 09 08

CC:N2

T E R C

Co-Principal Investigators

Susan Jo Russell

Karen Economopoulos

Authors

Lucy Wittenberg
Director Grades 3–5

Karen Economopoulos
Director Grades K–2

Virginia Bastable
(SummerMath for Teachers,
Mt. Holyoke College)

Katie Hickey Bloomfield

Keith Cochran

Darrell Earnest

Arusha Hollister

Nancy Horowitz

Erin Leidl

Megan Murray

Young Oh

Beth W. Perry

Susan Jo Russell

Deborah Schifter
(Education
Development Center)

Kathy Sillman

Administrative Staff

Amy Taber
Project Manager

Beth Bergeron

Lorraine Brooks

Emi Fujiwara

Contributing Authors

Denise Baumann

Jennifer DiBrienza

Hollee Freeman

Paula Hooper

Jan Mokros

Stephen Monk
(University of Washington)

Mary Beth O'Connor

Judy Storeygard

Cornelia Tierney

Elizabeth Van Cleef

Carol Wright

Technology

Jim Hammerman

Classroom Field Work

Amy Appell

Rachel E. Davis

Traci Higgins

Julia Thompson

Collaborating Teachers

This group of dedicated teachers carried out extensive field testing in their classrooms, met regularly to discuss issues of teaching and learning mathematics, provided feedback to staff, welcomed staff into their classrooms to document students' work, and contributed both suggestions and written material that has been incorporated into the curriculum.

Bethany Altchek

Linda Amaral

Kimberly Beauregard

Barbara Bernard

Nancy Buell

Rose Christiansen

Chris Colbath-Hess

Lisette Colon

Kim Cook

Frances Cooper

Kathleen Drew

Rebeka Eston Salemi

Thomas Fisher

Michael Flynn

Holly Ghazey

Susan Gillis

Danielle Harrington

Elaine Herzog

Francine Hiller

Kirsten Lee Howard

Liliana Klass

Leslie Kramer

Melissa Lee Andrichak

Kelley Lee Sadowski

Jennifer Levitan

Mary Lou LoVecchio

Kristen McEnaney

Maura McGrail

Kathe Millett

Florence Molyneaux

Amy Monkiewicz

Elizabeth Monopoli

Carol Murray

Robyn Musser

Christine Norrman

Deborah O'Brien

Timothy O'Connor

Anne Marie O'Reilly

Mark Paige

Margaret Riddle

Karen Schweitzer

Elisabeth Seyferth

Susan Smith

Debra Sorvillo

Shoshanah Starr

Janice Szymaszek

Karen Tobin

JoAnn Trauschke

Ana Vaisenstein

Yvonne Watson

Michelle Woods

Mary Wright

Note: Unless otherwise noted, all contributors listed above were staff of the Education Research Collaborative at TERC during their work on the curriculum. Other affiliations during the time of development are listed.

Advisors

Deborah Lowenberg Ball,
University of Michigan

Hyman Bass, Professor of Mathematics and Mathematics Education
University of Michigan

Mary Canner, Principal, Natick Public Schools

Thomas Carpenter, Professor of Curriculum and Instruction,
University of Wisconsin-Madison

Janis Freckmann, Elementary Mathematics Coordinator,
Milwaukee Public Schools

Lynne Godfrey, Mathematics Coach,
Cambridge Public Schools

Ginger Hanlon, Instructional Specialist in Mathematics,
New York City Public Schools

DeAnn Huinker, Director, Center for Mathematics and
Science Education Research, University of Wisconsin-Milwaukee

James Kaput, Professor of Mathematics, University of
Massachusetts-Dartmouth

Kate Kline, Associate Professor, Department of Mathematics
and Statistics, Western Michigan University

Jim Lewis, Professor of Mathematics,
University of Nebraska-Lincoln

William McCallum, Professor of Mathematics,
University of Arizona

Harriet Pollatsek, Professor of Mathematics,
Mount Holyoke College

Debra Shein-Gerson, Elementary Mathematics Specialist,
Weston Public Schools

Gary Shevell, Assistant Principal,
New York City Public Schools

Liz Sweeney, Elementary Math Department,
Boston Public Schools

Lucy West, Consultant, Metamorphosis:
Teaching Learning Communities, Inc.

This revision of the curriculum was built on the work of the many authors who contributed to the first edition (published between 1994 and 1998). We acknowledge the critical contributions of these authors in developing the content and pedagogy of *Investigations*:

Authors

Joan Akers

Michael T. Battista

Douglas H. Clements

Karen Economopoulos

Marlene Kliman

Jan Mokros

Megan Murray

Ricardo Nemirovsky

Andee Rubin

Susan Jo Russell

Cornelia Tierney

Contributing Authors

Mary Berle-Carman

Rebecca B. Corwin

Rebeka Eston

Claryce Evans

Anne Goodrow

Cliff Konold

Chris Mainhart

Sue McMillen

Jerrie Moffet

Tracy Noble

Kim O'Neil

Mark Ogonowski

Julie Sarama

Amy Shulman Weinberg

Margie Singer

Virginia Woolley

Tracey Wright

Contents

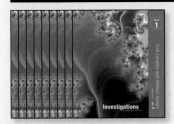

C U R R I C U L U M

Overview of Program Components

FOR TEACHERS

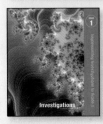

The **Curriculum Units** are the teaching guides. (See far right.)

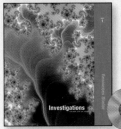

Implementing Investigations in Grade 1 offers suggestions for implementing the curriculum. It also contains a comprehensive index.

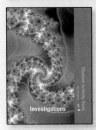

The **Resources Binder** contains all the Resource Masters and Transparencies that support instruction. (Also available on CD) The binder also includes a student software CD.

FOR STUDENTS

The **Student Activity Book** contains the consumable student pages (Recording Sheets, Homework, Practice, and so on).

The **Student Math Handbook** contains Math Words and Ideas pages and Games directions.

The *Investigations* Curriculum

Investigations in Number, Data, and Space® is a K–5 mathematics curriculum designed to engage students in making sense of mathematical ideas. Six major goals guided the development of the *Investigations in Number, Data, and Space®* curriculum. The curriculum is designed to:

- Support students to make sense of mathematics and learn that they can be mathematical thinkers

- Focus on computational fluency with whole numbers as a major goal of the elementary grades

- Provide substantive work in important areas of mathematics—rational numbers, geometry, measurement, data, and early algebra—and connections among them

- Emphasize reasoning about mathematical ideas

- Communicate mathematics content and pedagogy to teachers

- Engage the range of learners in understanding mathematics

Underlying these goals are three guiding principles that are touchstones for the *Investigations* team as we approach both students and teachers as agents of their own learning:

1. *Students have mathematical ideas.* Students come to school with ideas about numbers, shapes, measurements, patterns, and data. If given the opportunity to learn in an environment that stresses making sense of mathematics, students build on the ideas they already have and learn about new mathematics they have never encountered. Students learn that they are capable of having mathematical ideas, applying what they know to new situations, and thinking and reasoning about unfamiliar problems.

2. *Teachers are engaged in ongoing learning* about mathematics content, pedagogy, and student learning. The curriculum provides material for professional development, to be used by teachers individually or in groups, that supports teachers' continued learning as they use the curriculum over several years. The *Investigations* curriculum materials are designed as much to be a dialogue with teachers as to be a core of content for students.

3. *Teachers collaborate with the students and curriculum materials* to create the curriculum as enacted in the classroom. The only way for a good curriculum to be used well is for teachers to be active participants in implementing it. Teachers use the curriculum to maintain a clear, focused, and coherent agenda for mathematics teaching. At the same time, they observe and listen carefully to students, try to understand how they are thinking, and make teaching decisions based on these observations.

Investigations is based on experience from research and practice, including field testing that involved documentation of thousands of hours in classrooms, observations of students, input from teachers, and analysis of student work. As a result, the curriculum addresses the learning needs of real students in a wide range of classrooms and communities. The investigations are carefully designed to invite all students into mathematics—girls and boys; members of diverse cultural, ethnic, and language groups; and students with a wide variety of strengths, needs, and interests.

Based on this extensive classroom testing, the curriculum takes seriously the time students need to develop a strong conceptual foundation and skills based on that foundation. Each curriculum unit focuses on an area of content in depth, providing time for students to develop and practice ideas across a variety of activities and contexts that build on each other. Daily guidelines for time spent on class sessions, Classroom Routines (K–3), and Ten-Minute Math (3–5) reflect the commitment to devoting adequate time to mathematics in each school day.

About This Curriculum Unit

This **Curriculum Unit** is one of nine teaching guides in Grade 1. The fifth unit in Grade 1 is *Fish Lengths and Animal Jumps*.

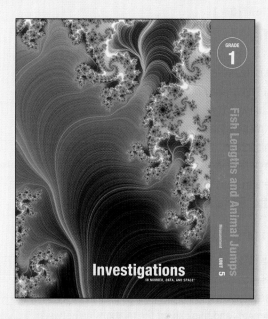

- The **Introduction and Overview** section organizes and presents the instructional materials, provides background information, and highlights important features specific to this unit.

- Each Curriculum Unit contains several **Investigations.** Each Investigation focuses on a set of related mathematical ideas.

- Investigations are divided into one-hour **Sessions,** or lessons.

- Sessions have a combination of these parts: **Activity, Discussion, Math Workshop, Assessment Activity,** and **Session Follow-Up.**

- Each session also has one or more **Classroom Routines** that are done outside of math time.

- At the back of the book is a collection of **Teacher Notes** and **Dialogue Boxes** that provide professional development related to the unit.

- Also included at the back of the book are the **Student Math Handbook** pages for this unit.

- The **Index** provides a way to look up important words or terms.

Overview

Investigation	Session	Day	
INVESTIGATION 1 **Learning to Measure** Students develop accurate measurement techniques as they measure the length of various objects using several different units, including inch tiles. They describe lengths that fall between two whole numbers and discuss why measurements of the same object when measured with the same unit should be equal. Students solve comparison problems where they compare a measured length to a target length and they solve story problems which involve finding the difference between two lengths.	**1.1** Cube Towers and Measuring Collections	1	
	1.2 Measuring with Cubes, Tiles, or Paper Clips	2	
	1.3 Measuring Fish	3	
	1.4 Fish Stories	4	
	1.5 Measuring Keepers	5	
	1.6 Assessment: How Long Is This Fish?	6	
INVESTIGATION 2 **Measuring Distances** Students measure lengths using units of various sizes. They discuss how different-sized units result in different measurements and think about the relationship between the size of the unit and the total number of units needed to measure a length. Students continue to solve comparison problems, measuring lengths to determine not only which is longer but how much longer. Throughout the investigation, they refine their measurement skills.	**2.1** Measuring with Kid Steps	7	
	2.2 Measuring with Different Units	8	
	2.3 Measuring with Different Units, *continued*	9	
	2.4 Measuring Jumps	10	
	2.5 End-of-Unit Assessment	11	

Each *Investigations* session has some combination of these five parts: **Activity, Discussion, Math Workshop, Assessment Activity,** and **Session Follow-Up.** These session parts are indicated in the chart below. Each session also has one or more **Classroom Routines** that are done outside of math time.

Activity	Discussion	Math Workshop	Assessment Activity	Session Follow-Up
● ●	●			●
● ●	●			●
● ●	●			●
●	●	●		●
●	●	●		●
	●	●	●	●
●	●			●
●	●			●
● ●	●			●
●	●	●		●
	●	●	●	●

Classroom Routines

Morning Meeting	Start With/ Get To	Quick Images	Quick Surveys
●	●		
●	●		
●		●	
●			●
●	●		
●			
●	●		
●	●		
●		●	
●			●
●	●		

Mathematics

IN THIS UNIT

Fish Lengths and Animal Jumps is the fifth of nine units in the Grade 1 sequence. The activities in this unit help students develop:

- An understanding of what length is

- A sense of linear measurement

- A foundation of skills for accurate linear measurement using nonstandard and standard units

 LOOKING BACK This unit builds on the work done in kindergarten with linear measurement. That work focused on making direct comparisons to determine longer than and shorter than and having students use nonstandard units to measure lengths of familiar objects.

The activities in this unit focus on 3 mathematical emphases:

1 Linear Measurement Understanding length

Math Focus Points

- ◆ Understanding what length is and how it can be measured

- ◆ Measuring lengths using different-sized units

- ◆ Identifying the longest dimension of an object

- ◆ Comparing lengths to determine which is longer

- ◆ Identifying contexts in which measurement is used

- ◆ Understanding the meaning of *at least* in the context of linear measurement

In this unit, students measure lengths up to 18 inches in the first investigation and turn to measuring considerably larger lengths in the second investigation. They learn that length measurement is applied to objects and to distances.

It is important for students to develop a sense of how measurement is used and when it is helpful in the real world. This unit involves students in a realistic context in which measuring is used, that of measuring fish to determine whether they are "*keepers*". In this context, students grapple with the idea of *at least as long as,* an idea that is as important in measurement as it is in number operations.

2 Linear Measurement Using linear units

Math Focus Points

- ◆ Developing accurate measurement techniques

- ◆ Describing measurements that are *in between* whole numbers of units

- ◆ Understanding that measurements of the same length should be the same when they are measured twice or by different people using the same unit

- ◆ Understanding that measuring an object using different-length units will result in different measurements

- ◆ Measuring length by iterating a single unit

The focus of the unit is on developing a foundation of skills for accurate linear measurement. These include knowing where to start and stop measuring, understanding how measuring tools must be lined up so that there are no gaps or overlaps, knowing which dimension to measure, measuring the shortest line from point to point, and understanding that many measurements are not reported in whole numbers.

The idea that many measurements are not reported in whole numbers is critical because measurement is not the same as counting. When measuring, the focus is on describing a continuous quantity (in this case, length). First graders need to learn that accurate descriptions of length often involve nuances such as "a little more than _____," "a little less than _____," "between 15 and 16 cubes," or even "15 and a half cubes." This may be one of students' first experiences with quantities that are not whole numbers.

Regardless of what is measured, students learn that when one measures an object twice—or when two different people measure it—the same results should be obtained, assuming that the same unit is used. This idea of *reliability* is important in mathematics, science, and social science.

What happens when something is measured with small units versus larger units? This question is dealt with in both investigations. Students begin to see that measuring an object in cubes will result in a different count than will measuring the same object in inch tiles or paper clips. The idea that, when measuring a given object, "larger units result in smaller numbers" is an important one, but it is not one that most first graders can grasp. Students explore the notion that different-sized units will result in different counts, and a few students will begin to see the inverse relationship between size of unit and number of units needed to cover a distance. This idea will be explored more fully in the second grade measurement unit.

3 Linear Measurement Measuring with standard units

Math Focus Points

◆ Using inch tiles to measure objects in inches

Finally, students are shown real measurement tools used by adults, and they work with inches (inch tiles) as units when they are measuring fish, books, and objects in the classroom. First graders need to be introduced to some of the units that adults use when they are measuring. However, the focus is not on learning to read conventional measurement tools because considerable research has shown that early emphasis on reading rulers results in a great deal of confusion. Typically, students can read the numbers but don't fully understand what the numbers mean in a measurement context. For that reason, the focus of these two investigations is on learning to use consistent units to measure accurately and to understand the underlying mathematics of measuring.

This Unit also focuses on

◆ Solving problems about comparing lengths

Classroom Routines focus on

◆ Developing strategies for counting accurately

◆ Using the calendar as a tool for keeping track of time

◆ Developing vocabulary to talk about time (morning, noon, midday, afternoon, etc.) and sequence (*first, next, last, before, after, and so on*)

◆ Collecting and recording data

◆ Connecting written numbers and number names

◆ Using the 100 chart as a tool for counting

◆ Practicing the forward and backward counting sequences with numbers up to 60

◆ Developing and analyzing visual images for quantities

◆ Identifying and naming coins

◆ Collecting, counting, representing, describing, and comparing data

◆ Interpreting different representations of data including: pictures, bar graphs, tallies, and Venn diagrams

LOOKING FORWARD

In second grade, students will continue to work on these issues and further refine their measurement techniques. They will clarify the idea that not only will they get different counts when using different units to measure an object but also that the smaller unit will yield the larger count. Students will be introduced to rulers with particular attention to the concepts that underlie the structure of the ruler, as well as techniques for using rulers. Students will also work with the two standard systems of measurement—English and metric—and develop a sense of the lengths of inches, feet, centimeters, and meters.

Assessment

IN THIS UNIT

ONGOING ASSESSMENT: Observing Students at Work

The following sessions provide **Ongoing Assessment: Observing Students at Work** opportunities:

- **Session 1.1, p. 26**
- **Session 1.2, p. 31**
- **Session 1.3, pp. 38 and 40**
- **Session 1.4, pp. 45 and 46**
- **Session 1.5, p. 49**
- **Session 1.6, p. 54**
- **Session 2.1, p. 65**
- **Session 2.2, p. 72**
- **Session 2.3, pp. 74 and 76**
- **Session 2.4, p. 80**
- **Session 2.5, p. 83**

WRITING OPPORTUNITIES

The following sessions have **writing** opportunities for students to explain their mathematical thinking:

- **Session 1.4, pp. 44–45**
  Student Activity Book, pp. 11–12
- **Session 2.3, p. 75**
  Student Activity Book, p. 23
- **Session 2.4, p. 80**
  Student Activity Book, pp. 26–27

PORTFOLIO OPPORTUNITIES

The following sessions have work appropriate for a **portfolio:**

- **Session 1.4, pp. 44–45**
  Student Activity Book, pp. 11–12

- **Session 1.6, p. 53**
  M28, Assessment: How Long Is
  This Fish?

- **Session 2.3, p. 75**
  Student Activity Book, p. 23

- **Session 2.4, p. 80**
  Student Activity Book, pp. 26–27

- **Session 2.5, p. 83**
  M34, End-of-Unit Assessment

Assessing the Benchmarks

Observing students as they engage in conversation about their ideas is a primary means to assess their mathematical understanding. Consider all of your students' work, not just the written assessments. See the chart below for suggestions about key activities to observe.

 Checklist Available

Benchmarks in This Unit	Key Activities to Observe	Assessment
1. Demonstrate accurate measuring techniques when measuring a distance with nonstandard or standard units. These techniques include starting at the beginning, ending at the end, leaving no gaps or overlaps, measuring in a straight line, and keeping track of the number of units.	**Session 1.1:** Measuring with Connecting Cubes **Session 1.2:** Measuring with Cubes, Tiles, or Paper Clips **Sessions 1.3–1.6:** Measuring Fish **Session 2.1:** Measuring with Kid Steps	**Session 1.6:** How Long Is This Fish? ✓ **Sessions 2.2–2.3:** Big Steps, Little Steps, and Craft Sticks **Sessions 2.4–2.5:** Animal Jumps ✓
2. Know at least one way of describing a measurement that falls between two whole numbers.	**Session 1.1:** Measuring with Connecting Cubes **Session 1.2:** Measuring with Cubes, Tiles, or Paper Clips **Sessions 1.3–1.6:** Measuring Fish **Session 2.1:** Measuring with Kid Steps	**Session 1.6:** How Long Is This Fish? ✓ **Sessions 2.2–2.3:** Big Steps, Little Steps, and Craft Sticks **Sessions 2.4–2.5:** Animal Jumps
3. Understand that the same result should be obtained when the same object is measured twice or when two different people measure the same object (using the same unit).	**Session 1.1:** Measuring with Connecting Cubes **Session 1.3:** Kim Measures a Fish	**Session 1.6:** How Long Is This Fish? ✓
4. Understand that measuring with different-sized units will result in different numbers.	**Sessions 2.2–2.3:** Big Steps, Little Steps, and Craft Sticks **Session 2.3:** What Did We Find?	**Session 2.5:** End-of-Unit Assessment

Relating the Mathematical Emphases to the Benchmarks

Mathematical Emphases	Benchmarks
Linear Measurement Understanding length	1, 2, 3, 4
Linear Measurement Using linear units	1, 2, 3
Linear Measurement Measuring with standard units	3

Classroom Routines

Classroom Routines offer practice and review of key concepts for this grade level. These daily activities, to be done in ten minutes outside of math class, occur in a regular rotation every 4–5 days. Specific directions for the day's routine are provided in each session. For the full description and variations of each classroom routine see *Implementing Investigations in Grade 1.*

Morning Meeting

Students continue to use the calendar to keep track of time and events, collect and analyze data about the weather, and count the number of students in the class. Variations focus on reviewing different times of day.

Math Focus Points

◆ Developing strategies for counting accurately

◆ Using the calendar as a tool for keeping track of time

◆ Developing vocabulary to talk about time (morning, noon, midday, afternoon, etc.) and sequence (first, next, last, before, after, etc.)

◆ Collecting and recording data

Start With/Get To

Students count *from* a number between 31 and 60, *to* a number between 0 and 30 on the 100 chart. Then they practice counting forward and backward with numbers 1 to 60 on the 100 chart.

Math Focus Points

◆ Connecting written numbers and number names

◆ Using the 100 chart as a tool for counting

◆ Practicing the forward and backward counting sequences with numbers up to 60

Quick Images

Students see groups of coins. They determine the total amount and identify the type of each coin.

Math Focus Points

◆ Developing and analyzing visual images for quantities

◆ Identifying and naming coins

Quick Survey

Students collect, organize, record, and discuss data about the class.

Math Focus Points

◆ Collecting, counting, representing, describing, and comparing data

◆ Interpreting different representations of data including: pictures, bar graphs, tallies, and Venn diagrams

Practice and Review

IN THIS UNIT

Practice and review play a critical role in the *Investigations* program. The following components and features are available to provide regular reinforcement of key mathematical concepts and procedures.

Books	Features	In This Unit . . .
Curriculum Unit	**Classroom Routines** offer practice and review of key concepts for this grade level. These daily activities, to be done in ten minutes outside of math class, occur in a regular rotation every 4–5 days. Specific directions for the day's routine are provided in each session. For the full description and variations of each classroom routine see *Implementing Investigations in Grade 1*.	• **All sessions**
Student Activity Book	**Daily Practice** pages in the *Student Activity Book* provide one of three types of written practice: **reinforcement** of the content of the unit, **ongoing review,** or **enrichment** opportunities. Some Daily Practice pages will also have Ongoing Review items with multiple-choice problems similar to those on standardized tests.	• **All sessions**
	Homework pages in the *Student Activity Book* are an extension of the work done in class. At times they help students prepare for upcoming activities.	• **Session 1.3** • **Session 2.1**
Student Math Handbook	**Math Words and Ideas** in the *Student Math Handbook* are pages that summarize key words and ideas. Most Words and Ideas pages have at least one exercise.	• **Student Math Handbook, pp. 93–107**
	Games pages are found in a section of the *Student Math Handbook*.	• **No games are introduced in this unit.**

Differentiation

Supporting the Range of Learners

Sessions	1.1	1.2	1.3	1.4	2.1	2.3	2.4
Intervention		•	•	•	•		•
Extension		•			•		•
ELL	•		•	•	•	•	

Intervention

Adjustments to the activities are provided to support students who may need additional practice or who may benefit from alternate teaching strategies.

Extension

Adjustments to the activities are provided to support students who may finish early or who may be ready for more challenging or enriching activities.

English Language Learners (ELL)

In this unit, students learn how to apply linear measurements to length as well as distance. Because many measurements are not reported in whole numbers, students need to be comfortable with expressions such as *at least, a little more than, a little less than, between ____ and ____,* and *____ and à half.* You can support English Language Learners by emphasizing these terms in class discussions and activities, and encouraging them to use this new vocabulary in context.

In Investigation 1, when students use cubes to measure the lengths of objects, English Language Learners may need help understanding the expressions *beginning, end,* and *in between.* To demonstrate the everyday meanings of these terms, have students stand in a line and describe their positions. [Danielle] is at the *beginning* of the line. [Vic] is at the *end* of the line. [Sacha] is *in between* [Emilia]

and [Toshi]. You can test students' understanding by asking them to switch places. Then ask English Language Learners to practice these expressions by giving each other commands. To emphasize the measurement-related meanings of these terms, you can think aloud as you help students measure various objects and encourage them to think aloud about their own measurements.

In Units 1 and 2, students learned to compare size (*big/ bigger/biggest*) and quantity (*few/fewer/fewest*). In this unit, they compare length (*long/longer*) and distance (*far/farther*). Before beginning Investigation 2, it would be helpful to review the comparative language structures introduced in the previous units and to model these structures with new vocabulary from the current unit.

Working with the Range of Learners: Classroom Cases is a set of episodes written by teachers that focuses on meeting the needs of the range of learners in the classroom. In the first section, *Setting up the Mathematical Community,* teachers write about how they create a supportive and productive learning environment in their classrooms. In the next section, *Accommodations for Learning,* teachers focus on specific modifications they make to meet the needs of some of their learners. In the last section, *Language and Representation,* teachers share how they help students use representations and develop language to investigate and express mathematical ideas. The questions at the end of each case provide a starting point for your own reflection or for discussion with colleagues. See *Implementing Investigations in Grade 1* for this set of episodes.

Mathematical Emphases

Linear Measurement Understanding length

Math Focus Points

◆ Understanding what length is and how it can be measured

◆ Measuring lengths using different-sized units

◆ Identifying the longest dimension of an object

◆ Identifying contexts in which measurement is used

◆ Understanding the meaning of *at least* in the context of linear measurement

Linear Measurement Using linear units

Math Focus Points

◆ Developing accurate measurement techniques

◆ Describing measurements that are *in between* whole numbers of units

◆ Understanding that measurements of the same lengths should be the same when they are measured twice or by different people using the same unit

◆ Understanding that measuring an object using different-length units will result in different measurements

Linear Measurement Measuring with standard units

Math Focus Points

◆ Using inch tiles to measure objects in inches

This Investigation also focuses on

◆ Solving problems about comparing lengths

Learning to Measure

	Student Activity Book	Student Math Handbook	Professional Development: Read Ahead of Time
SESSION 1.1 p. 22			
Cube Towers and Measuring Collections Students measure various objects by using connecting cubes. They compare measurements and make decisions about how to record a measurement that is in between whole numbers of cubes.	1–2	94, 95, 96; 100–101	• **Mathematics in This Unit,** p. 10 • **Teacher Note:** Learning About Length, p. 87; Talking About Partial Units, p. 89 • **Dialogue Box:** Measuring with Partial Units, p. 97
SESSION 1.2 p. 28			
Measuring with Cubes, Tiles, or Paper Clips Using cubes, tiles, or paper clips, students practice measuring objects from the Measurement Collections. They discuss their measuring techniques.	3–4	96, 97–98	
SESSION 1.3 p. 34			
Measuring Fish Students hear a story about a girl who makes a number of measurement errors. They are asked to identify and correct the errors. Then they measure the lengths of fish in inches to determine which ones meet specific length requirements.	5–9	93, 95, 97–98, 99, 102	

Classroom Routines See page 14 for an overview.

Morning Meeting	*Quick Images*
• No materials needed	• Class set of overhead coins
Start With/Get To	*Quick Survey*
• *Start With/Get To* cards 1–100	• *Quick Survey* chart for Session 1.4.
• 100 chart	See instructions on page 41.
• 2 baskets	

Materials to Gather	Materials to Prepare
• **Connecting cubes** (about 40 per pair)	• **Measurement Collections** Put together a collection of 8 items for every 4 or 5 students. Items should be 2–18 inches long. Each collection should be the same. (For example, if each collection contains a box, all the boxes should be the same length.) Possible items to include: an unsharpened pencil, scissors, stapler, a book, an empty box, a wooden building block, a paper cup, a marker, a postcard or greeting card. Label each item with masking tape. • **M1–M2, Family Letter** Make copies. (1 per student)
• **Color tiles** (about 10) • **Book to measure** (1 per class) • **Measurement Collections** (1 per 4–5 students;	• **Measuring Materials** Assemble small sets of measuring materials for each group of 4 or 5 students. Each group will need connecting cubes, color tiles, and paper clips, about 40 of each. • **M3–M4, Family Letter** Make copies. (1 per student)
• **Large self-stick notes** (2 per pair) • **Color tiles** (about 25 per pair) • **T36, Kim's Fish** 📠 • **T37–T40, How Kim Measured** 📠 • **Measurement Collections** (as needed; from Session 1.1) • **Measuring materials** (as needed; from Session 1.2) • **Glue or transparent tape** (1 per class)	• **M5, Kim's Fish** Make copies. (1 per pair) • **M10–M14, Fish Set 1: Perch; M15–M20, Fish Set 2: Mackerel; M21–M26, Fish Set 3: Alewife** Copy and cut out sets of Perch, Mackerel, and Alewife. Each set includes 6 fish of different sizes. Prepare enough sets so that students can work in pairs. (You may choose to copy the fish onto cardstock and/or laminate the copies.) • **12″ x 9″ envelopes** Prepare an envelope for each fish set. Attach a label to each envelope with the name of the fish and the length it has to be to be a keeper. • **M27, Measuring Keepers** Make copies. (2 per student plus extras for use during this Investigation) • **Measurement Collections** Add new items to the collections prepared for Session 1.1. (as needed)

📠 Overhead Transparency

Learning to Measure,
continued

	Student Activity Book	Student Math Handbook	Professional Development: Read Ahead of Time
SESSION 1.4 p. 41			
Fish Stories The class works together on a story problem about fish. In Math Workshop, students work on developing measurement techniques and solving comparison problems.	5–6, 11–13	102, 107	• **Dialogue Box:** Understanding Comparison Problems, p. 98 • **Teacher Note:** Strategies to Solve Comparison Problems, p. 90
SESSION 1.5 p. 48			
Measuring Keepers Students are introduced to a Math Workshop, Making Keepers, to work on measurement techniques. Class discussion focuses on solution methods for solving comparison story problems.	5–6, 11–12, 14	97–98, 102, 107	
SESSION 1.6 p. 52			
Assessment: How Long Is This Fish? Students work on an assessment question: How Long Is This Fish? Then they practice their measurement techniques in Math Workshop. The session concludes with a discussion of the assessment question.	15	97–98, 100–101	• **Teacher Note:** Assessment: How Long Is This Fish?, p. 92

Materials to Gather	Materials to Prepare
• **M27, Measuring Keepers** (as needed; from Session 1.3) • **T41, Mackerel Fish A** 🖨 • **T42, Mackerel Fish F** 🖨 • **Fish Sets** (1 per pair; from Session 1.3) • **Color tiles** (about 25 per pair)	• **Chart paper** On a sheet of chart paper, write the fish story problem about Kim as shown in Session 1.4, p. 43. • **Chart paper: "Measuring"** Divide the chart paper into two columns, and label them "Challenges" and "Tips."
• **M27, Measuring Keepers** (as needed; from Session 1.3) • **12″ x 18″ sheets of paper** (1 per student) • **Markers and other drawing materials** (as needed) • **Color tiles** (about 25 per pair) • **Fish Sets** (1 per pair; from Session 1.3) • **Chart paper**	• **Chart paper** On a sheet of chart paper, write Fish Story 1 from *Student Activity Book,* p. 11.
• **M27, Measuring Keepers** (as needed; from Session 1.3) • **Color tiles** (about 25 per pair) • **Fish Sets** (1 per pair; from Session 1.3) • **Markers and other drawing materials** (as needed) • **T43, Assessment: How Long Is This Fish?** 🖨	• **M28, Assessment: How Long Is This Fish?** Make copies. (1 per student) • **M29, Assessment Checklist: Measurement Techniques** ✓ Make copies as needed.

🖨 Overhead Transparency   ✓ Checklist Available

Cube Towers and Measuring Collections

Math Focus Points

◆ Understanding what length is and how it can be measured

◆ Identifying the longest dimension of an object

◆ Describing measurements that are *in between* whole numbers of units

◆ Understanding that measurements of the same lengths should be the same when they are measured twice or by different people using the same unit

Vocabulary

measure
length
measurement

Today's Plan		Materials
ACTIVITY **1** **Introducing Measuring with Connecting Cubes**	15 MIN CLASS	• Measurement Collections* • Connecting cubes
ACTIVITY **2** **Measuring with Connecting Cubes**	30 MIN PAIRS	• *Student Activity Book*, p. 1 • Measurement Collections* • Connecting cubes
DISCUSSION **3** **How Long Is It?**	15 MIN CLASS	• *Student Activity Book*, p. 1 • Measurement Collections* • Connecting cubes
SESSION FOLLOW-UP **4** **Daily Practice**		• *Student Activity Book*, p. 2 • *Student Math Handbook*, pp. 94, 95, 96, 100–101 • M1–M2, Family Letter

*See *Materials to Prepare*, p. 19.

Classroom Routines

Start With/Get To: Counting Backward In this variation of *Start With/Get To*, the *start with* basket holds cards numbered 31–60, and the *get to* basket holds cards numbered 1–30. Choose a card from each of the baskets and ask students to find and mark the numbers from each card on the 100 chart. As a class, count backward from the *start with* number to the *get to* number.

ACTIVITY

① Introducing Measuring with Connecting Cubes

15 MIN   CLASS

Professional Development
❶ **Teacher Note:** Learning About Length, p. 87

Gather students where they can see one another and a Measurement Collection, perhaps in a circle on the floor or on chairs with the objects in the center of the circle. In the first part of this session, you will establish what the longest dimension of an object is.

Suppose that I wanted to measure the longest part of this [bottle]. Where would I measure? What's the longest part?

Ask for volunteers to identify the longest part of the object. As students indicate which dimension they think is longest, run your finger along that dimension.

Let's try another one. Suppose that I wanted to find out the longest part of this [box of tissues]. Where would I measure? Why do you think that it is the longest part?

Once again, ask for volunteers to show where to measure. If students have trouble understanding what you mean by *the longest part* of an object, choose a few more especially long items from the collection (or elsewhere in the classroom). For each, ask students to identify the longest dimension.

Today you will work with a partner to measure the length, or the longest part, of things I have collected for our Measurement Collection. We are going to use connecting cubes to measure these things.❶

Choose an object from the Measurement Collection, and ask students what part you should measure. Ask students for predictions about how many cubes long this object is. Then demonstrate making a train of cubes and putting the cubes next to the object to measure its length.

For this first demonstration, make the cube train shorter than the object and begin measuring from the middle of the object, and see whether students correct you.

- pick objects from all around the classroom (4) for each group.

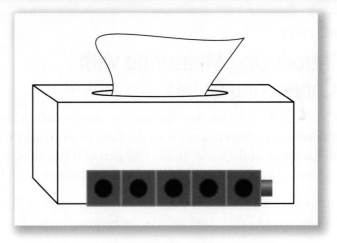

I've made a cube train to measure how long this is. Is this right? When I count these cubes, will it tell me how long this [box] is? Why or why not?

If students note the error in your measuring technique, have them explain where you need to place the start of the cube train and where the end should be. Then restate this idea yourself. If students do not point out your error, explain that to measure the object, the cube train must be placed so that it starts at one end of the object and ends at the other end.

When you measure an object, you have to be sure to start at one end of the object and finish as close to the other end as you can.

Ask students to count how many cubes long your object is. Then record the name of the object and its length in cubes on the board. The object is unlikely to be an exact number of cubes in length and it is important to help students notice this. Ask students for ideas on describing the length when it is not exact.

*This isn't exactly [10] cubes long. How long should we say it is?*❷ ❸

Students might say:

"It's a little longer than 10 cubes."

"It's about 10 and a half cubes long."

ACTIVITY

② Measuring with Connecting Cubes

30 MIN   PAIRS

Have students turn to *Student Activity Book* page 1, and explain the activity to them.

You will work with a partner to measure things from the Measurement Collection. Choose an object, and write its name on the sheet. Let's say that your first object is a [stapler]. Measure it by making a train of cubes that is as long as it is and record that measurement on your sheet. You and your partner need to agree on how long it is. If it is *in between* different numbers of cubes, decide how you will write this.❹

Explain to students that they will repeat this process as they measure each object in the Measurement Collection with connecting cubes.

Remind students of the importance of lining up the connecting cubes next to the object in order to measure accurately.

As students do their measurements and find objects that are between whole numbers of cubes, help them figure out ways of writing numbers between whole numbers. Include the standard notation for $4\frac{1}{2}$ to remind students of this representation of a length that seems to be midway between 4 and 5.

Measuring lengths that are between whole numbers helps students to learn how to label partial units.

Name _____ Date _____

Fish Lengths and Animal Jumps

How Many Cubes Long?

Name of Object	How long?
	_____ cubes
	_____ cubes
	_____ cubes
	_____ cubes
	_____ cubes
	_____ cubes
	_____ cubes
	_____ cubes

Which is your shortest object? _____

Which is your longest object? _____

Make a list of your objects from shortest to longest.

© Pearson Education 1

Session 1.1   Unit 5 ①

▲ **Student Activity Book, p. 1**

Differentiation

❹ **English Language Learners** In this activity and during the following discussion, students need to understand expressions such as *beginning, end, a little more than, a little less than,* and *in between*. As you circulate, think aloud with English Language Learners while helping them measure an object or two. Let's see how many cubes long this stapler is. We need to put the first cube at the *beginning* of the stapler, and then line up the cubes until we get to the *end*. Hmm...the stapler is *a little more than*

- make
  measurement
    chart.

ONGOING ASSESSMENT: Observing Students at Work

This activity will give you some initial information about students' measuring techniques.

- **Do students identify the longest dimension to measure?**

- **Do students align the beginning and end of a cube or train with the edges of the object they are measuring?**

- **Do students double-check when they are not sure of their measurements?**

- **Do students count accurately and keep track of the number of cubes?**

- **How do students show lengths that are in between whole numbers of cubes?**

③ DISCUSSION
How Long Is It?

15 MIN CLASS

Math Focus Points for Discussion

◆ Describing measurements that are *in between* whole numbers of units

◆ Understanding that measurements of the same lengths should be the same when they are measured twice or by different people using the same unit

After students have measured four or more objects with their partner (as time allows), take an object that several people have measured (such as a stapler), and show it to the class.

You'll have more chances to work with the Measurement Collection in the next few days, but let's check in and see how people are measuring. Who measured the [stapler]? How many cubes long is it?

Ask one pair of students who have measured the [stapler] to check on *Student Activity Book* page 1 and read their results. Ask them to show how they measured the [stapler].

[Tamika] and [Nicky] found that the [stapler] was a little more than 7 cubes long. Do you agree? Who else measured the [stapler]?

Ask other students who have measured the same object to give their measurements. It is possible, even likely, that these measurements will not be the same. Use this opportunity to explore the reasons for the differences.

[Bruce] and [Seth] found that it was 8 cubes long. Show us how you measured. Why do you think [Bruce] and [Seth] got different results from [Tamika] and [Nicky]?

If students got the same numbers for their measurements, say something like the following:

[Deshawn] said that the pencil is between 6 and 7 cubes long, and [Shaquana] said that it's almost 7. Can they both be right? Why?

What if someone came in and measured the same pencil and told us that it's a little more than 8 long? Remember, [Deshawn] said that it's between 6 and 7 cubes long, and [Shaquana] said that it's almost 7. Can they all be right? Why not?

If everyone is measuring carefully and measuring the same way with cubes, we should get the same number for the length. Sometimes we might use different words to say it. There are different ways to name the same length. One person might say 6 cubes and a little more, and someone else might say $6\frac{1}{2}$ cubes. These are different ways to name the same length.

As time allows, show another object and ask pairs of students who have measured it to give their results and explain how they measured. Talk about the reasons for differences, and emphasize the importance of measuring carefully. ❺

Teaching Note

❺ **Initial Experiences** Students will be working with these important ideas in measurement throughout this unit. Treat this discussion as an introductory one, knowing that students will return to these ideas over and over again.

▲ **Student Activity Book, p. 2**

SESSION FOLLOW-UP

④ Daily Practice

 Daily Practice: For ongoing review, have students complete *Student Activity Book* page 2.

 Student Math Handbook: Students and families may use *Student Math Handbook* pages 94, 95, 96, 100–101 for reference and review. See pages 101–104 in the back of this unit.

 Family Letter: Send home copies of the Family Letter (M1–M2).

Measuring with Cubes, Tiles, or Paper Clips

Math Focus Points

◆ Measuring lengths using different-sized units

◆ Developing accurate measurement techniques

◆ Understanding that measurements of the same lengths should be the same when they are measured twice or by different people using the same unit

◆ Understanding that measuring an object using different-length units will result in different measurements

Vocabulary

unit

Today's Plan			Materials
ACTIVITY **① Introducing New Units to Measure With**	🕐 15 MIN	👥 CLASS	• Measuring materials* • Book to measure
ACTIVITY **② Measuring with Cubes, Tiles, or Paper Clips**	🕐 30 MIN	🧍 INDIVIDUALS	• *Student Activity Book*, p. 3 • Measurement Collections (from Session 1.1)
DISCUSSION **③ Measuring Accurately**	🕐 15 MIN	👥 CLASS	• *Student Activity Book*, p. 3 • Measurement Collection (from Session 1.1)
SESSION FOLLOW-UP **④ Daily Practice**			• *Student Activity Book*, p. 4 • *Student Math Handbook*, pp. 96, 97–98 • M3–M4, Family Letter

*See *Materials to Prepare,* p. 19.

Classroom Routines

Start With/Get To: Counting Backward Choose a *start with* number from the first basket (cards 31–60) and a *get to* number from the second (cards 1–30). Ask students to find and mark both numbers on the 100 chart. As a class, count from the *start with* number backward to the *get to* number.

ACTIVITY

① Introducing New Units to Measure With

15 MIN CLASS

In this activity, you will show students how to measure the length of a book with inch tiles.

Last time we talked about and measured the longest parts of objects. Suppose that we wanted to figure out how long this book is. Look carefully at the book I'm holding. What part of this book is the longest?

As you did in the previous session, talk about one of the sides being longer than the other, and the other side being shorter. Point out that the length of a book is its long edge.

When we measure length, we go in a straight line along the long edge of the object.

Explain to students that in today's math class, they will be measuring the objects in the Measurement Collection by using tiles and paper clips in addition to connecting cubes. Show students the set of measuring materials.

I'm going to measure the length of this book with tiles. How do you suppose I might measure it with tiles? Where should I start?

Put the book where everyone can see it, and hold up a tile.❶

Where should I put the first tile?

As you put the tile on the book, point out that you start at the edge of the book.

Where should I put the second tile?

As you place the second tile next to the first one, tell students that it is important that the tiles be as close to one another as possible. Ask for a couple of volunteers to come up and place the remaining tiles, making sure that each new tile touches the previous tile.

Students practice lining up tiles side by side as they measure the length of a book.

Where should we stop? How do we figure out how long the book is?

As students say how long the book is, record their measurements on the board. Next to the number you record for the measurement, be sure to write the word *tiles*.

It is likely that the object will be in between whole numbers of tiles. As in the previous session, ask what to do with the in-between length.

Students may say "between 10 and 11 tiles," or "10 tiles plus some more," or "less than 11 tiles," or even "10 and $\frac{1}{2}$ tiles." When the idea of $\frac{1}{2}$ arises, explain that $\frac{1}{2}$ means that it is in the middle of the tile and record $\frac{1}{2}$ on the board.

We have all of these different ways to write how long the book is. [Chris] said it's between 10 and 11 tiles. [Leah] said that it's 10 tiles plus some more. Can they both be right? Why?

What if [Toshi] said it's a little less than 11 tiles and that someone else said that it's more than 12 tiles? Can they both be right? Why not?

Before ending the discussion, explain the importance of identifying the unit used to measure.

When you are measuring your objects today, you will be using tiles or cubes or paper clips. It could get confusing if we don't know which unit we used to measure. I'm writing *tiles* so that we know that we used tiles to measure this book.

ACTIVITY

② Measuring with Cubes, Tiles, or Paper Clips

30 MIN INDIVIDUALS

Tell students to look at *Student Activity Book* page 3.

You will work by yourselves to measure objects from the Measurement Collection. Today you can use cubes or tiles or paper clips to measure. Choose an object, and write its name on *Student Activity Book* page 3. Then measure it. Write how long it is, and be sure to say whether you used cubes or tiles or paper clips. If it is in between different numbers, decide how you will show this.

ONGOING ASSESSMENT: Observing Students at Work

Students measure various objects with cubes, tiles, and paper clips.

- **Do students start at the beginning of the object and finish at the end?** Do they line up the units without leaving any gaps?

- **Do they count accurately and keep track of the number of units correctly?**

- **Do students double-check when they are not sure of their measurements?**

- **How do students record measurements that are in between whole numbers?**

DIFFERENTIATION: Supporting the Range of Learners

Intervention Students may have more difficulty working with tiles and paper clips than they have with connecting cubes. Because cubes connect, it is easier to line them up without leaving gaps. If students have motor challenges when they line up tiles or paper clips, either suggest that they first use connecting cubes or show them ways of lining up objects more precisely.

Extension Students who finish quickly could measure the same objects using a second unit.

Name ___ Date ___
Fish Lengths and Animal Jumps

How Long Is It?

Name of Object	How long?	What did you use?		
		cubes	tiles	clips
		cubes	tiles	clips
		cubes	tiles	clips
		cubes	tiles	clips
		cubes	tiles	clips
		cubes	tiles	clips

Session 1.2 Unit 5 3

▲ Student Activity Book, p. 3

DISCUSSION

③ Measuring Accurately

15 MIN   CLASS

Math Focus Points for Discussion

◆ Developing accurate measurement techniques

◆ Understanding that measurements of the same lengths should be the same when they are measured twice or by different people using the same unit

◆ Understanding that measuring an object using different-length units will result in different measurements

Gather students together, making sure that they have their completed *Student Activity Book* page 3. Have available a set of measuring materials. Also have available three different objects from the Measurement Collection to use as references. Include one very small object, one large object, and one in-between object.

This [box] is very big! What part of this [box] is the length? Did anyone measure the length of this [box]?

Ask for a volunteer to show how they measured the length of the object. Ask questions such as the following as the volunteer demonstrates:

• Where did you start measuring?

• Where did you finish?

• How did you line up the [cubes, tiles, paper clips]?

• How did you keep track of all of the units?

• What did you do when you got to the end of the [box] and your measurement wasn't a whole number of units?

• What was the hardest thing about measuring this object?

Ask whether someone else measured the [box] with the same unit.

Did you get the same measurement for this [box] or a different measurement? Why was that?

If students who used the same unit got different results, ask them to explain why they might have gotten different amounts. Have them show how they measured to resolve the differences. If all of the students who used the same unit got the same measurement, point this out.

If some students used a different unit to measure the same object, have them show how they measured the length of the object.

Students can use different units to measure length.

This is very interesting. [Leah] measured the length of the box and got [18 connecting cubes]. [Toshi] measured the length of the same box and got [15 tiles]. Why is that?❷

Repeat this process for all three objects if time allows.

SESSION FOLLOW-UP
4 Daily Practice

 Daily Practice: For reinforcement of this unit's content, have students complete *Student Activity Book* page 4.

 Student Math Handbook: Students and families may use *Student Math Handbook* pages 96, 97–98 for reference and review. See pages 101–104 in the back of this unit.

 Family Letter: Send home copies of Family Letter (M3–M4).

Math Note

❷ **The Size of the Unit Matters** The main mathematical idea you are discussing is that when you use different-sized units to measure, you will get different results. Most first graders will not yet understand that bigger units result in smaller measurements, but they should begin to get the idea that the size of the unit matters. They should also understand that it is not a *mistake* when different numbers are obtained with different units.

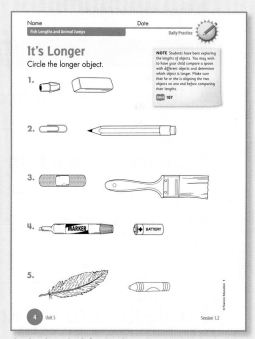

▲ **Student Activity Book, p. 4**

Measuring Fish

Math Focus Points

◆ Identifying contexts in which measurement is used

◆ Using inch tiles to measure objects in inches

◆ Developing accurate measurement techniques

◆ Understanding the meaning of *at least* in the context of linear measurement

Vocabulary

inch

Today's Plan

		Materials
① DISCUSSION **Measurement Contexts** 10 MIN CLASS		• Color tiles
② ACTIVITY **Kim Measures a Fish** 20 MIN CLASS PAIRS		• T36–T40 ⬚; M5 • Large self-stick notes; color tiles
③ ACTIVITY **Measuring Fish** 30 MIN CLASS PAIRS		• *Student Activity Book*, pp. 5–6 • M10–M14*; M15–M20*; M21–M26*; M27* • 12″ x 9″ envelopes*; glue or transparent tape
④ SESSION FOLLOW-UP **Daily Practice and Homework**		• *Student Activity Book*, pp. 7–9 • *Student Math Handbook*, pp. 93, 95, 97–98, 99, 102

*See *Materials to Prepare*, p. 19.

Classroom Routines

Quick Images: Coins Using the set of overhead coins, display 1 penny, 1 nickel, 1 dime, and 1 quarter. Follow the basic *Quick Images* activity. Discuss the quantity and type of coins with the class. Ask questions that focus on identifying each coin and the total number of coins such as:

• Which coin is the [penny]?

• What is the name of *this* coin?

• How many [nickels] did you see?

• How do you know?

If time permits, repeat using 2 pennies, 2 nickels and 2 dimes. For a full write-up of this variation, see *Part 4: Classroom Routines* in *Implementing Investigations in Grade 1: Quick Images*.

DISCUSSION
Measurement Contexts

10 MIN   CLASS

Math Focus Points for Discussion

◆ Identifying contexts in which measurement is used

Begin the discussion by asking students to think about times or situations in which they have needed to measure something or have seen an adult measure something.

We've been measuring things in our classroom to find out how long they are. It's very important to know the length of things. If I wanted to move a piano into our classroom through the door, how could measurement help?

Talk about the fact that heavy or large objects are difficult to move and that measurement can help you tell whether something will fit in a space properly.

Measurement is important to find out whether things are the right size. Has anyone ever gone fishing? When people catch a fish, they measure it to see whether it is long enough to keep. You can't keep a baby fish, and you can't ask a fish how old it is, but you can tell if it's a grown-up fish by measuring how long it is. When a fish is long enough to keep, it's called a *keeper*.

Today and tomorrow, we're going to measure pictures of fish to see whether they are keepers. We're going to measure with inch tiles because people often use inches to see whether a fish is a keeper.

Hold up a color tile, and explain that they are also called inch tiles because each side is one inch long. Then show the class the size of an inch between your thumb and index finger. Ask students to show you how big an inch is by holding up their thumbs and index fingers. Look around to make sure that the size is about right.

Can you think of something that is about one inch long? ❶

Teaching Note

❶ **About one inch long?** As students share ideas about items they think are about one inch long, ask the rest of the class if they agree that the suggested items are about one inch in length. Students may suggest items such as a quarter, a toe, a paper clip, a button, or an eraser.

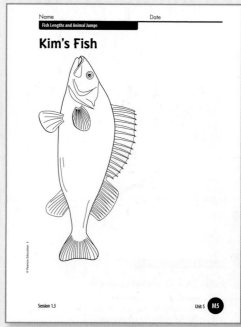

Name _____   Date _____

Fish Lengths and Animal Jumps

Kim's Fish

Session 1.3   Unit 5 **M5**

▲ Resource Masters, M5; T36

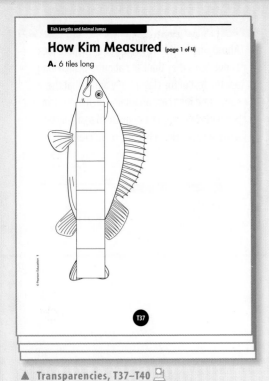

▲ Transparencies, T37–T40

▲ Resource Masters, M10–M14

20 MIN · CLASS · PAIRS

ACTIVITY

② Kim Measures a Fish

Before you read the story "Kim Measures a Fish," as presented below, have transparencies of Kim's Fish (T36) and each of the examples of Kim's measurement techniques, How Kim Measured (T37–T40), ready to show at the appropriate times.

Before you start measuring your own fish pictures, let's talk about Kim, who has gone fishing and has caught a perch.

Show a transparency of Kim's Fish (T36).

This is a picture of a perch, a kind of fish.

Kim has been measuring her fish with inch tiles to see whether it is long enough to keep.

The first time Kim measured the fish, she found that it was 6 inch tiles long.

Show a transparency of How Kim Measured (T37).

The second time she measured it, she found that it was 8 tiles long.

Show a transparency of How Kim Measured (T38).

"That's strange," she thought. "I got two different numbers. I wonder why."

Show the pictures again, and count the tiles aloud with students for each example.

Kim counted the right number of tiles, but she got different results. Why do you think she got different numbers of tiles when she measured?

Students should notice that in A, Kim did not measure from the tip of the nose to the end of the tail. In B, Kim did not measure in a straight line across the fish.

Talk to someone next to you about what Kim could have done differently to get a measurement that's right.

After students have talked to a partner for a minute, continue with the story.

Kim wasn't happy with her measurements because she got 6 inches the first time and 8 inches the next. She knew that her measurements should be the same. So she tried measuring again. This time, she was careful to begin and end in the right places. This time, she got 5 tiles!

Show a transparency of How Kim Measured (T39).

Stop again, and ask the class why Kim got fewer tiles when she measured her fish this time. Most students should recognize that Kim did not measure with the tiles edge to edge across the fish. Emphasize that the tiles measure 1 inch from side to side, not corner to corner.

Kim was getting frustrated. "It's hard to get so many different answers." She tried again, and this time she definitely measured in a straight line, and she started at the beginning and ended at the end. She measured 4 inches.

Show a transparency of How Kim Measured (T40).

"I think this is pretty good" she told her teacher. "I think this fish is 4 inches long. But I'm not really sure."

What do you think? Is Kim's fish really 4 inches long?

Students should notice the gaps between tiles. If not, draw their attention to these gaps. Ask whether the fish is longer or shorter than 4 inches.

Finally, finish the story.

Kim needs our help. She was getting tired of so much measuring. She has one question, "How long is this fish, REALLY?"

Give each pair of students a copy of Kim's Fish (M5), 2 self-stick notes, and some tiles.

This fish is the same size as Kim's fish. You and your partner will also measure this fish with 1-inch tiles. When you've finished and you're sure of your answer, write it on a self-stick note with a marker and bring it to me.

Learning to measure correctly is an important skill students learn in this unit.

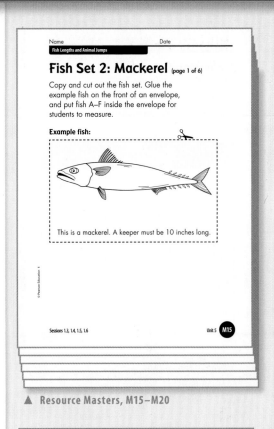

▲ Resource Masters, M15–M20

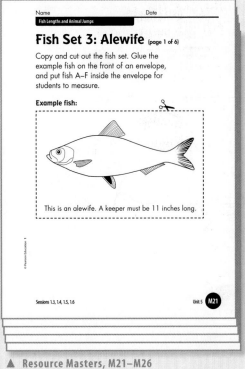

▲ Resource Masters, M21–M26

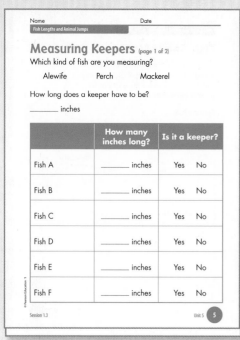

▲ Student Activity Book, pp. 5–6;
Resource Masters, M27

As students bring you their notes, arrange them in order according to the number of tiles counted.

Call students together again, and repeat the question that Kim asked.

How long *is* this fish?

Show a transparency of Kim's Fish (T36). Review the measurements that students made, and ask one pair to demonstrate with tiles on the transparency. Most students should have gotten the same results (about 7 tiles). As you have in the previous sessions, talk about different ways to name the same length.

When most of us get the same results, as long as we measured correctly, we can be pretty sure that we have a correct measurement. We found that Kim's fish is 7 inches long.

To be a keeper, a perch must be at least 6 inches long. Is Kim's fish a keeper? Is Kim's fish at least 6 inches long? Yes; Kim can keep her fish and eat it for dinner tonight.

ONGOING ASSESSMENT: Observing Students at Work

This activity will give you a sense of how accurately students understand *length*. Pay particular attention to whether students are making any of the mistakes Kim made.

- **Do students start measuring at the beginning and stop at the end of the picture?**

- **Do students leave any gaps between units?**

- **Do they measure the length of the fish in a straight line?**

DIFFERENTIATION: Supporting the Range of Learners

Intervention If students are having trouble doing this measurement, it is a sign that more practice is needed. You may want to set up additional Math Workshop time with the Measurement Collection, adding some new objects.

ACTIVITY

③ Measuring Fish

30 MIN CLASS PAIRS

Students continue to develop their measuring skills.

Now you are going to start measuring your own fish to see whether they are keepers. Like Kim, you will be measuring with 1-inch tiles because people often use inches to see whether a fish is a keeper.

Hold up a tile, and reiterate to students that we call them inch tiles because they are one inch long on each side.

Hold up the life-size picture of the alewife, Fish Set 3: Alewife Fish C (M23).

This is an alewife, which many people fish for in New England. Let's say that alewives need to be 11 inches long to be keepers. How would we measure this to tell whether it is a keeper?

Ask students to give you suggestions for measuring the fish. Talk about measuring from one end of the fish to the other, which, for the alewife, will be from the tip of the fish's lower lip to the tip of its tail. It is fine to measure to either section of the tail.

Remember that the fish has to be *at least* 11 inches long to be a keeper. It can be longer, but it cannot be shorter. Let's count the tiles while I measure.❷

This fish is a little less than 10 inches long. It is not a keeper. I have to put this fish back in the water.

I am going to give you envelopes that have pictures of different kinds of fish in them. Some envelopes have alewives, some have mackerel, and some have perch. On the outside of the envelope, it says what kind of fish are in it and how long they have to be in order to be *keepers*. Each fish has a letter. Your job is to measure the fish with inch tiles and find the keepers. Then record your findings on *Student Activity Book* page 5.

When you finish the page for one kind of fish, I will give you an envelope with a different fish that you may use with *Student Activity Book* page 6. You'll work on this today and tomorrow.

❷ **English Language Learners** During this activity, check in with English Language Learners to be sure that they understand the expression *at least _____ inches long.* Remember, the fish you keep must be *at least* 11 inches long. That means they must be *exactly* 11 inches long or *more than* 11 inches long. Is this fish *exactly* 11 inches? Is it *less than* 11 inches or *more than* 11 inches? **If students are still struggling with the language, you can help them visualize the concept by laying out a row of 11 one-inch tiles and measuring various "fish" against it.**

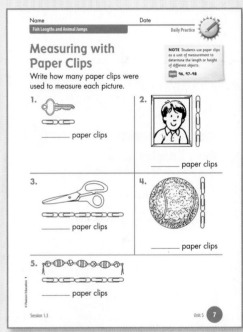

▲ **Student Activity Book, p. 7**

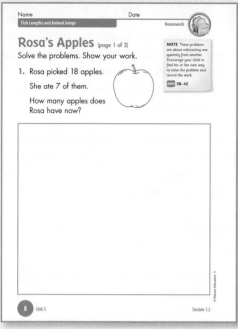

▲ Student Activity Book, p. 8

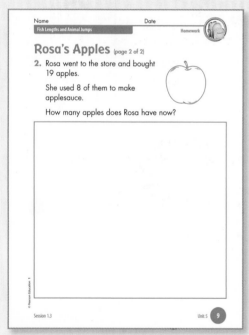

▲ Student Activity Book, p. 9

Students use inch tiles to measure the lengths of fish.

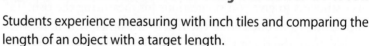

ONGOING ASSESSMENT: Observing Students at Work

Students experience measuring with inch tiles and comparing the length of an object with a target length.

- **Do students understand the concept of *at least* in the context of measurement?**

- **Are students using good measurement techniques? Are their measurements accurate?**

- **Do students use the word *inch* to refer to the length of the tile and as the measure for determining the length of keepers?**

SESSION FOLLOW-UP
4 Daily Practice and Homework

 Daily Practice: For reinforcement of this unit's content, have students complete *Student Activity Book* page 7.

 Homework: Students will work on *Student Activity Book* pages 8 and 9, which have two subtraction story problems for students to solve at home. Remind students to record their solution strategies.

 Student Math Handbook: Students and families may use *Student Math Handbook* pages 93, 95, 97–98, 99, 102 for reference and review. See pages 101–104 in the back of this unit.

Fish Stories

Math Focus Points

◆ Solving problems about comparing lengths

◆ Understanding the meaning of *at least* in the context of linear measurement

◆ Developing accurate measurement techniques

Vocabulary

height

Today's Plan			Materials
ACTIVITY ❶ Introducing Fish Story Problems	15 MIN	CLASS	• T41–T42 • Color tiles; chart paper with the fish story written on it*

MATH WORKSHOP
❷ Fish Problems
  ❷ⒶMeasuring Fish
  ❷ⒷFish Stories
	30 MIN		❷Ⓐ • *Student Activity Book,* pp. 5–6 (from Session 1.3)
			• M27
			• Fish Sets (from Session 1.3)
			❷Ⓑ • *Student Activity Book,* pp. 11–12

DISCUSSION ❸ Measuring Fish	15 MIN	CLASS	• Chart paper: "Measuring"*
SESSION FOLLOW-UP ❹ Daily Practice			• *Student Activity Book,* p. 13 • *Student Math Handbook,* pp. 102, 107

*See *Materials to Prepare,* p. 21.

Classroom Routines

Quick Survey: Water or Juice? Quick Survey is a new routine designed to continue the work of *What Would You Rather Be?* On chart paper write the question "Would you rather drink water or juice?" Then, below the question, create a 2-column table with the headings "Water" and "Juice." Use a "w" or a "j" to record the students' responses and then count them. After counting responses, have a short discussion about the results of the survey. For a full write-up of this routine see *Part 4: Classroom Routines* in *Implementing Investigations in Grade 1:* Quick Survey.

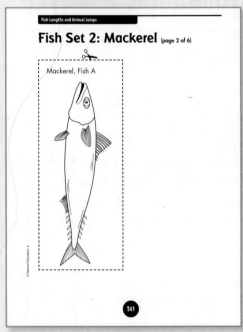

Fish Lengths and Animal Jumps

Fish Set 2: Mackerel (page 2 of 6)

Mackerel, Fish A

T41

▲ **Transparencies, T41**

---

1 Introducing Fish Story Problems

To introduce these comparison story problems, begin with a context familiar to students: comparing heights. Ask two students of different heights to stand together in front of the class.

Let's look at [Felipe's] and [Edgar's] heights—how tall they are. Who is taller—[Felipe] or [Edgar]? (Edgar) How much taller is [Edgar]? Show me with your hands how much taller [Edgar] is than [Felipe].

If students have difficulty understanding the question, find other ways to phrase it. For example, you might ask,

How much more would [Felipe] need to grow to be as tall as [Edgar] is right now?

Have a student come up to [Felipe] and [Edgar] to show how much taller [Edgar] is than [Felipe]. The student should show the vertical distance over [Felipe's] head to reach the level of the top of [Edgar's] head.

Students compare heights as an introduction to comparing lengths.

Show the transparencies of Mackerel Fish A (T41) and Mackerel Fish F (T42) to the class, one over the other, with the mouths lined up. **1**

Let's ask the same question about two fish. Take a look at these two mackerels. Which is longer, Fish A or Fish F? How much longer is Fish F than Fish A? Show me with your hands.

Ask a student or two to show on the transparencies how much longer Fish F is than Fish A.

How many inches do you think that is? How many inches does Fish A need to grow to be as long as Fish F? Remember, an inch tile is 1 inch long from side to side.

Have a student place inch tiles to show how much longer Fish F is than Fish A (about 4 inches). Students might say that Fish F is about 4 inches longer than Fish A.

Show students the story problem you wrote on chart paper. Do not tell students ahead of time that they can solve the problem by subtracting. Just present the problem and discuss what is happening.❷

I would like everyone to think about this story problem for a minute. I don't want you to solve it yet. Close your eyes, and imagine the situation.

> Kim caught an alewife that is 7 inches long.
>
> Then she caught a mackerel that is 10 inches long.
>
> How much longer is the mackerel than the alewife?

Who can tell us what you see?

It is particularly important for students to imagine what is happening in comparison situations. This visualizing technique becomes very important in helping students understand what is happening in the problem.

After a couple of volunteers have shared what they think is happening, pose the following questions:

In this problem, what are we trying to find out?

What information do we already know?

Do you think the answer to this problem will be more than or less than 10 inches? Why?

Because this problem does not involve a straightforward action, students may be unsure of exactly what is happening or how to solve it. By asking them to visualize the problem and think about whether the answer is more or less than 10 inches, you help them make sense of the problem.

Teaching Note

❷ **Solving Story Problems** Students will be familiar with the process of visualizing and then describing the action from their work with solving addition and subtraction problems in previous units.

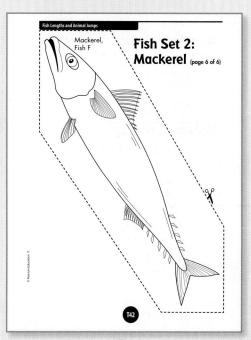

Fish Lengths and Animal Jumps

Mackerel, Fish F

Fish Set 2: Mackerel (page 6 of 6)

T42

▲ Transparencies, T42

Professional Development

❸ **Dialogue Box:** Understanding Comparison Problems, p. 98

❹ **Teacher Note:** Strategies to Solve Comparison Problems, p. 90

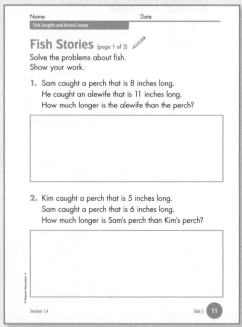

Name _____ Date _____

Fish Lengths and Animal Jumps

Fish Stories (page 1 of 2)
Solve the problems about fish.
Show your work.

1. Sam caught a perch that is 8 inches long.
   He caught an alewife that is 11 inches long.
   How much longer is the alewife than the perch?

2. Kim caught a perch that is 5 inches long.
   Sam caught a perch that is 6 inches long.
   How much longer is Sam's perch than Kim's perch?

Session 1.4   Unit 5   11

▲ **Student Activity Book, p. 11**

Next ask all the students to solve the problem by using tiles. Even though some students may be able to solve the problem without using tiles, it is important that everyone demonstrate it with tiles to visualize the situation.

Spend a few minutes figuring out how many more tiles Kim's alewife would need to grow to be as long as the mackerel:

After a few minutes ask students to share how they would solve the problem.

Students might say:

"I know that I need to count out 7 tiles and 10 tiles but then I do not know how to finish the problem."

"I have to add on tiles to the 7 until they get to 10. I added on 3 tiles."

Have several students demonstrate the story problem with tiles to show how they know that the answer is 3 inches.

Today during Math Workshop you will have a chance to solve more Fish Story Problems, similar to the one we just did. You will work in pairs on these problems. One of you will read the problem aloud while the other one closes your eyes to picture what the problem is about. Then you talk about what the problem says before solving it. ❸ ❹

Show students *Student Activity Book* pages 11–12, Fish Stories, and read through the problems together.

② MATH WORKSHOP
Fish Problems

30 MIN

Students work on two activities in which they use their measuring skills.

②A Measuring Fish

PAIRS

For complete details about this activity, see Session 1.3, pages 39–40. When students finish *Student Activity Book* pages 5 and 6, give them a copy of Measuring Keepers (M27) and an envelope for another kind of fish.

ONGOING ASSESSMENT: Observing Students at Work

Students gain experience measuring with inch tiles and comparing the length of an object with a target length. As students work on this task, be alert for challenges they encounter, and plan to discuss these at the end of the session. Also, observe the following:

- **Are students measuring from the tip of one end to the tip of the other end?**
- **Do students show evidence that they understand the concept of *at least*?**
- **Are students accurately counting the inch tiles?**
- **Are students recording their findings correctly?**
- **Are students developing a sense of how long an inch is?**

DIFFERENTIATION: Supporting the Range of Learners

Intervention Some students may benefit from making a set of tiles the length that represents a keeper for the type of fish they are working on. Then, they may directly compare each of the fish with this *standard* set of tiles.

2B Fish Stories

PAIRS

Students work in pairs to solve the story problems about comparing lengths of fish. They read the problem aloud, ⑤ visualize it, solve the problem, and then check their solution. Each student records his or her solution method on *Student Activity Book* pages 11–12 in a way that someone else can understand.

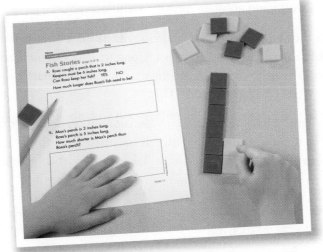

Students can use tiles to solve comparison problems.

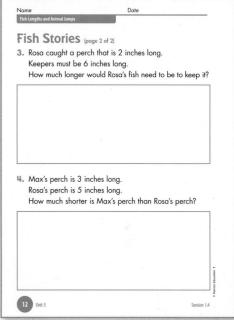

Name _____ Date _____

Fish Lengths and Animal Jumps

Fish Stories (page 2 of 2)

3. Rosa caught a perch that is 2 inches long.
   Keepers must be 6 inches long.
   How much longer would Rosa's fish need to be to keep it?

4. Max's perch is 3 inches long.
   Rosa's perch is 5 inches long.
   How much shorter is Max's perch than Rosa's perch?

12 Unit 5   Session 1.4

▲ **Student Activity Book, p. 12**

ONGOING ASSESSMENT: Observing Students at Work

These story problems offer students an experience to help the students make sense of and solve comparison situations.

- **Do students understand what the problem is asking and what they need to do to solve the problem?**

- **How do students figure out how much longer or shorter one fish is than the other?** Do they arrange lengths of tiles and compare them? Do they count on or count back?

DIFFERENTIATION: Supporting the Range of Learners

Intervention Comparison problems are often very challenging for first graders. If students do not understand what is being asked or if they simply add the two numbers, have them close their eyes and listen to the problem as you read it. Then have them explain what the situation is. Have them show with tiles the lengths of the two fish and then ask how much longer the [perch] would need to be in order to be the same length as the [alewife]. Note that Problem 3 asks students to compare a 2-inch perch with the required length of a keeper, which is a more abstract idea. Here, too, you might have students show with tiles how long a perch needs to be to keep it.

DISCUSSION

15 MIN   CLASS

③ Measuring Fish

Math Focus Points for Discussion

◆ Developing accurate measurement techniques

At the end of the session, gather students for a discussion of the work they have done measuring fish. Conduct this as a *conference* that scientists who study fish might attend. Post the chart with columns headed "Challenges" and "Tips."

Scientists have to make many decisions about how to measure fish. The lengths of different fish tell scientists something about how many baby fish and adult fish live in lakes or in parts of the ocean.

Scientists are a little like us—they sometimes have trouble figuring out how to measure what they are studying. To learn how to measure better, they have conferences at which they talk about what is hard about measuring and share their ideas or *tips* for good measuring.

We're going to share what we found hard about measuring fish and also share our own tips for making good measurements of fish.

Ask students to contribute to the "Challenges" column first, and then ask for contributions to the "Tips" column. Use your own observations of students during the Workshop to make additions to the list.

At the end of the class session, post the chart paper where everyone can see it. Keep the chart up for reference during the upcoming assessment (Session 1.6).

Class discussions are a time to look at the difficulties students might have in measuring objects with odd shapes.

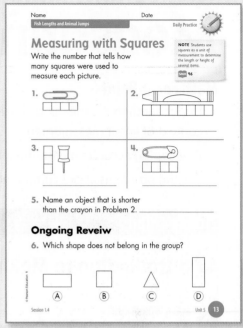

▲ **Student Activity Book, p. 13**

SESSION FOLLOW-UP
4 Daily Practice

 Daily Practice: For reinforcement of this unit's content, have students complete *Student Activity Book* page 13.

 Student Math Handbook: Students and families may use *Student Math Handbook* pages 102, 107 for reference and review. See pages 101–104 in the back of this unit.

Measuring Keepers

Math Focus Points

◆ Understanding the meaning of *at least* in the context of linear measurement

◆ Developing accurate measurement techniques

◆ Solving problems about comparing lengths

Today's Plan		Materials
ACTIVITY ❶ **Introduction to Making Keepers**	5 MIN CLASS	• 12″ x 18″ sheets of paper; markers and other drawing materials
MATH WORKSHOP ❷ **Measuring and Comparing** 2A **Making Keepers** 2B **Measuring Fish** 2C **Fish Stories**	40 MIN	2A • Students' partially-completed "Keepers" (from Activity 1) • Color tiles 2B • *Student Activity Book,* pp. 5–6 (Session 1.3) • M27 • Fish Sets (Session 1.3) 2C • *Student Activity Book,* pp. 11–12 (Session 1.4)
DISCUSSION ❸ **Fish Stories**	15 MIN CLASS	• Chart paper with Story Problem #1*; chart paper
SESSION FOLLOW-UP ❹ **Daily Practice**		• *Student Activity Book,* p. 14 • *Student Math Handbook,* pp. 97–98, 102, 107

*See *Materials to Prepare,* p. 21.

Classroom Routines

Start With/Get To: Counting Backward Choose a *start with* number from the first basket (cards 31–60) and a *get to* number from the second (cards 1–30). Ask students to find and mark both numbers on the 100 chart. Rather than counting as a whole class, students pair up and can either count together or take alternating turns.

ACTIVITY

① Introduction to Making Keepers

 5 MIN CLASS

Students begin a new fish activity that will continue during Math Workshop.

Today you will have a chance to invent a new fish and to decide how long a keeper is. Remember that we need to say how many inches long the fish needs to be to be a keeper. Show me with your fingers about how big an inch is.

Check to see whether students can identify approximately how long an inch is.

Now think about the fish you are going to invent, and decide what length a keeper will be. It can be any length that fits on this paper. (Show a sheet of 12″ x 18″ paper.)

Distribute the paper. Ask students to write their names on the top and to decide and write the length in inches that their keeper will be. When they have finished, have students set this task aside for now.

When you get to this activity during math workshop, you will draw one kind of fish that you invented. You need to draw a fish that is a keeper. You may also make up a name for your kind of fish.

MATH WORKSHOP

② Measuring and Comparing

 40 MIN

Students work on three activities in which they practice measuring techniques. If they have not finished *Student Activity Book* pages 11–12, they should work on those because students' answers to these problems will be discussed at the end of the session.

②A Making Keepers

 PAIRS

Students decide on a length for their fish and then draw a keeper of the fish they invented. They must measure their fish to make sure that it is in fact a keeper.

ONGOING ASSESSMENT: Observing Students at Work

As students work on this task, observe the following:

● **Do students understand the idea of *at least as long as*?** How is this evidenced when they draw their own fish? Do they put out a series of tiles to make sure that their fish is at least as long as this standard?

● **Are students able to accurately draw fish that are the length of keepers?**

Students draw their own keepers as they work on the concept of at least as long as.

2B Measuring Fish

PAIRS

For complete details about this activity, see Session 1.3, pages 39–40. When students finish *Student Activity Book* pages 5 and 6, give them a copy of Measuring Keepers (M27) and an envelope for another kind of fish.

2C Fish Stories

PAIRS

For complete details about this activity, see Session 1.4, pages 45–46.

15 MIN   CLASS

DISCUSSION

3 Fish Stories

Math Focus Points for Discussion

◆ Solving problems about comparing lengths

Meet together as a whole class to share solution strategies for the first problem on *Student Activity Book* page 11. Display the chart paper with the following problem:

> Sam caught a perch that is 8 inches long. He caught an alewife that is 11 inches long. How much longer is the alewife than the perch?

Use this discussion as an opportunity to model ways of recording a variety of solutions. Be sure to include someone who counted up from 8 to 11 or counted back from 11 to 8 and another who used a numerical strategy, such as 11 − ____ = 8 or 11 − 8 = 3. Have students demonstrate their thinking with tiles or cubes, as well as a number line.

Students might say:

 "I made a tower of 8 and one of 11. And 11 had 3 more cubes."

 "I counted from 8 to get to 11. 9, 10, 11—it's 3."

 "I found the number that I would subtract from 11 to get to 8."

As students share their strategies, record them on chart paper, using pictures, numbers, and/or equations. Some students will think of this problem as addition, and others may use a subtraction strategy. Both strategies are correct, depending on how students think about the problem.

SESSION FOLLOW-UP

④ Daily Practice

Daily Practice: For ongoing review, have students complete *Student Activity Book* page 14.

Student Math Handbook: Students and families may use *Student Math Handbook* pages 97–98, 102, 107 for reference and review. See pages 101–104 in the back of this unit.

Professional Development

❶ **Teacher Note:** Strategies to Solve Comparison Problems, p. 90

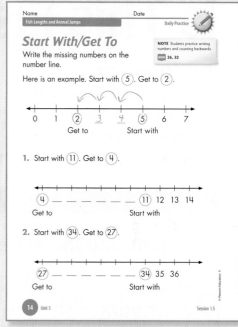

▲ **Student Activity Book, p. 14**

Assessment: How Long Is This Fish?

Math Focus Points

◆ Understanding that measurements of the same lengths should be the same when they are measured twice or by different people using the same unit

◆ Developing accurate measurement techniques

Today's Plan		Materials
ACTIVITY **1 Introducing the Assessment** 🕐 5 MIN CLASS		• M28
MATH WORKSHOP **2 Measuring Fish** 🕐 45 MIN **2A** Assessment: How Long Is This Fish? **2B** Measuring Fish **2C** Making Keepers		**2A** • M28, M29 ☑ • Color tiles **2B** • Fish Sets (from Session 1.3) • M27 **2C** • Students' partially-completed "Keepers" (from Session 1.5) • Markers and other drawing materials
DISCUSSION **3 How Long is This Fish?** 🕐 10 MIN CLASS		• T43 • Students' completed "Keepers" (from Activity 2C)
SESSION FOLLOW-UP **4 Daily Practice**		• *Student Activity Book,* p. 15 • *Student Math Handbook,* pp. 97–98, 100–101

Classroom Routines

Morning Meeting: Time of Day Follow your daily *Morning Meeting* Routine. During *Daily Schedule,* ask students to think about the times of day (morning, afternoon, etc.) at which daily activities happen, rather than just the sequence (first, next, last, etc.). For examples of questions to guide this discussion, see *Part 4: Classroom Routines* in *Implementing Investigations in Grade 1:* Morning Meeting.

ACTIVITY

① Introducing the Assessment

5 MIN   CLASS

Explain to students that today during Math Workshop, they will be meeting with you in a small group so that you can see how they are measuring with inch tiles. Show students the Assessment: How Long Is This Fish? (M28) and read the problem aloud to the class.

The first problem you need to work on involves measuring a fish with tiles and recording the length. The second question asks you to think about whether Kim's fish measurement could be right.

Explain to students that you are going to organize the class in three groups. While one group works with you, the other two groups will work on Math Workshop activities, Measuring Fish and Making Keepers. Let them know that as students finish working with you, you will call over students from another group to meet with you.

As you observe students working on this task, use Assessment Checklist: Measurement Techniques (M29) to record their measurement techniques.

MATH WORKSHOP

② Measuring Fish

45 MIN

For the rest of the session, students will continue to practice their measurement techniques.

②A Assessment: How Long Is This Fish?

GROUPS

Students complete this assessment in small groups. This problem assesses **Benchmark 2:** Know at least one way of describing a measurement that falls between two whole numbers, and **Benchmark 3:** Understand that the same result should be obtained when the same object is measured twice or when two people measure the same object (using the same unit).

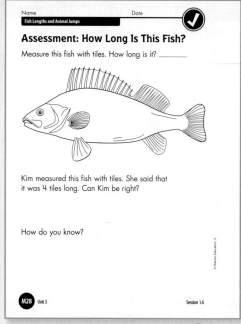

Name _____ Date _____
Fish Lengths and Animal Jumps

Assessment: How Long Is This Fish?

Measure this fish with tiles. How long is it? _____

Kim measured this fish with tiles. She said that it was 4 tiles long. Can Kim be right?

How do you know?

M28 Unit 5   Session 1.6

▲ Resource Masters, M28/T43 PORTFOLIO

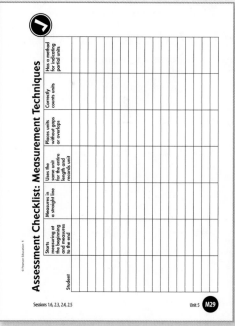

Assessment Checklist: Measurement Techniques

Sessions 1.6, 2.3, 2.4, 2.5   Unit 5 M29

▲ Resource Masters, M29

Professional Development

❶ Teacher Note: Assessment: How Long Is This Fish?, p. 92

As you observe how students measure the fish in problem 1, you are also gathering information about **Benchmark 1:** Demonstrate accurate measuring techniques when measuring with nonstandard units. You can record your observations on Assessment Checklist: Measurement Techniques (M29). Note that you will use this same Resource Master to record more information about this benchmark in Investigation 2.❶

As students finish, they can work on one of the other activities. Call over another group of students to complete the assessment.

Student	Starts measuring at the beginning and measures to the end.	Measures in a straight line.	Uses the same unit for the entire length and records unit.	Places units without gaps or overlaps.	Correctly counts units.	Has a method for indicating partial units.
Yanni	✓	✓	✓	✓	✓	✓ "a little less than"
Tamika	✓	✓	✓	✓	✓ counts by 2s	✓ Uses "1\2" notation.
Jonah	✓	✓	✓	Leaves gaps between units	✓	

ONGOING ASSESSMENT: Observing Students at Work

As students work on this assessment, look for the following:

- **Are students able to measure the fish accurately?** Do they place tiles from one end to the other, without gaps or overlaps?

- **Do students recognize that when different people measure the same object with the same unit, they should get the same measurement?**

2B Measuring Fish

PAIRS

For complete details about this activity, see Session 1.3, pages 39–40. Students can measure the set of fish that they have not yet worked with. They will need a copy of Measuring Keepers (M27).

2C Making Keepers

PAIRS INDIVIDUALS

For complete details about this activity, see Session 1.5, pages 49–50.

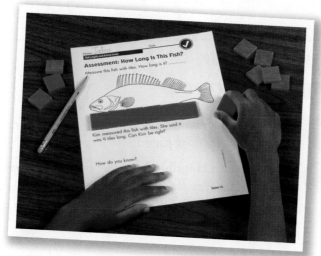

Students use tiles to learn accurate measuring techniques.

DISCUSSION

10 MIN CLASS

3 How Long Is This Fish?

Math Focus Points for Discussion

◆ Understanding that measurements of the same lengths should be the same when they are measured twice or by different people using the same unit

Begin the discussion by eliciting students' ideas about the assessment. Show a transparency of Assessment: How Long Is This Fish? (T43). Ask the students how long they think the fish is. Then have a student demonstrate with tiles how to measure the fish.

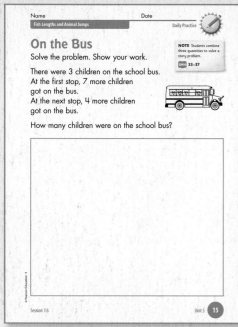

Name _____ Date _____

Fish Lengths and Animal Jumps   Daily Practice

On the Bus

Solve the problem. Show your work.

NOTE Students combine three quantities to solve a story problem.
SMH 33–37

There were 3 children on the school bus.
At the first stop, 7 more children got on the bus.
At the next stop, 4 more children got on the bus.

How many children were on the school bus?

Session 1.6   Unit 5   15

▲ **Student Activity Book, p. 15**

You have just measured this fish and found that it is between 6 and 7 tiles long. When Kim measured it, she found that it was 4 tiles long. Is Kim's answer right? How do you know?

Have students explain how they know that Kim's answer cannot be right. Ask whether they have any ideas about what Kim may have done wrong.

If there is still time, have some students share their invented fish from Math Workshop 2C, Making Keepers. Have them say how long a keeper is and how long their fish is.

SESSION FOLLOW-UP

4 Daily Practice

Daily Practice: For ongoing review, have students complete *Student Activity Book* page 15.

Student Math Handbook: Students and families may use *Student Math Handbook* pages 97–98, 100–101 for reference and review. See pages 101–104 in the back of this unit.

Mathematical Emphases

Linear Measurement Understanding length

Math Focus Points

◆ Measuring lengths using different-sized units

◆ Comparing lengths to determine which is longer

Linear Measurement Using linear units

Math Focus Points

◆ Developing accurate measurement techniques

◆ Describing measurements that are *in between* whole numbers of units

◆ Understanding that measuring an object using different-length units will result in different measurements

◆ Measuring length by iterating a single unit

This Investigation also focuses on

◆ Solving problems about comparing lengths

Measuring Distances

SESSION 2.1　　　　　　p. 62	Student Activity Book	Student Math Handbook	Professional Development: Read Ahead of Time	
Measuring with Kid Steps　Students discuss how to measure length by using toe-to-heel kid steps. They measure various lengths with kid steps and compare them. The concluding discussion focuses on their measurements of different distances and which distances are greater than others.	16–19	103, 105	• **Teacher Note:** Talking About Partial Units, p. 89 • **Dialogue Box:** More Measuring with Partial Units, p. 99	
SESSION 2.2　　　　　　p. 68				
Measuring with Different Units　Students measure lengths in the classroom by using the footprints of a baby, the footprints of a basketball player, and craft sticks as units. This activity, together with Animal Jumps in Sessions 2.4 and 2.5, provides opportunities to assess each student's measuring techniques.	16–17, 21–22	96–98, 103	• **Dialogue Box:** More Steps or Fewer?, p. 100	

Classroom Routines See page 14 for an overview.

Morning Meeting	Quick Images
• No materials needed	• Class set of overhead coins
Start With/Get To	**Quick Survey**
• *Start With/Get To* cards numbered 1–100	• Quick survey chart for Session 2.4. See instructions
• 1 basket	on page 78.
• Class 100 chart	

Materials to Gather	Materials to Prepare
• **Measuring tape, ruler, and yardstick** (1 of each)	• **Lengths of tape** Mark off 8 different straight lengths of tape on the floor that represent the distance from one point in the classroom to another, such as the distance from your desk to the door. These lengths should be placed in open areas so that children can walk on them (they should not be under furniture). Label the lengths A–H. Choose some distances that are similar in length so that students will be interested in comparing them to see which is longer. You can use electrical or masking tape (electrical is easier to remove), or you might mark the lengths with sidewalk chalk or tape down taut lengths of string or yarn.
• **M29, Assessment Checklist: Measurement Techniques** ☑ (as needed; from Session 1.6) • **Lengths of tape** (8; from Session 2.1) • **Craft sticks** (150–200) • **Markers** (8) • **12″ x 9″ envelopes** (4) • **10″ x 15″ envelopes** (4)	• **M30, Baby Steps** If you do not have the manufactured set of Baby Steps (Grade 1 card package), make 12 copies and cut out baby steps. Assemble four 12″ x 9″ envelopes with cutouts of baby steps, 27 steps per envelope. Cut out the rectangles, not around the actual footprints. Make sure that the lengths are cut accurately; the widths are not as important. • **M31–M32, Basketball Player Steps** If you do not have the manufactured set of Basketball Player Steps (Grade 1 card package), make 40 copies of M31 and M32 and cut out basketball player steps. Tape the two pieces together to make one basketball step. Assemble four 10″ x 15″ envelopes with cutouts of basketball player steps, 10 footprints per envelope. Cut out the rectangles, not around the actual footprints. Make sure that the lengths are cut accurately; the widths are not as important. • **M33, Measuring with Different Units** Make copies. (as needed) • **Measuring Stations** Set up three different measuring stations or tables, one with craft sticks, one with baby steps, and one with basketball player steps. • **Chart paper** Have 8 pieces of chart paper, one for each tape (A–H) representing a distance in the classroom. Make sure that the letter of the tape and what it measures is

☑ Checklist Available

Measuring Distances, *continued*

	Student Activity Book	Student Math Handbook	Professional Development: Read Ahead of Time	
SESSION 2.3 p. 73				
Measuring with Different Units, *continued* Students continue to measure lengths with different units. The discussion focuses on how different-sized units result in different measurements.	21, 23–24	96, 100–103		
SESSION 2.4 p. 78				
Measuring Jumps Math Workshop continues to focus on measuring lengths and solving combining and comparing word problems. The assessment of individual students' measuring techniques continues in the Animal Jumps activity.	25–28	100–101, 104–106		
SESSION 2.5 p. 82				
End-of Unit Assessment Students complete an activity that assesses students' understanding that, when measuring a given object, different-sized units yield different counts. Math Workshop continues. The session and the unit end with a discussion about measuring and comparing the lengths of animal jumps.	25–27, 29	96, 104–106	• **Teacher Note:** End-of-Unit Assessment, p. 95	

<table>
<tr><th>Materials to Gather</th><th>Materials to Prepare</th></tr>
<tr><td>

- **M29, Assessment Checklist** ☑ (as needed; from Session 1.6)
- **Materials for Measuring with Different Units**
  See Session 2.2.
- **Partially completed charts** (8; from Session 2.2)

</td><td></td></tr>
<tr><td>

- **M29, Assessment Checklist** ☑ (as needed; from Session 1.6)
- **Yardstick** (1)
- **Materials for Measuring with Different Units**
  See Session 2.2.
- **Counters** (as needed)

</td><td>

- **Animal Jump Tapes** Remove tapes from Session 2.1. Prepare Animal Jump Tapes that mark off new lengths. In each of two sections of the classroom, put down 6 pieces of tape as explained below. Write the names of the animals on these in marker. (Two sets of tapes are suggested so that more children can work on them at the same time.) Place the tapes in different directions so that the lengths can't be easily compared by looking at them. The lengths of tape (representing length of jump) are as follows: Frog—60 inches, 6 year old (Meredith)—53 inches, Jumping mouse—37 inches, Grasshopper—50 inches, Rabbit—55 inches, Squirrel—45 inches.

</td></tr>
<tr><td>

- **M29, Assessment Checklist** ☑ (as needed; from Session 1.6)
- **Lengths of tape** (12; from Session 2.4)
- **Materials for Measuring with Different Units**
  See Session 2.2.
- **Number line**
- **Counters** (as needed)

</td><td>

- **M34, End-of-Unit Assessment** Make copies. (1 per student)
- **Chart: "Animal Jumps"** Title a piece of chart paper "Animal Jumps." Divide the chart into three columns: Animal, Baby Steps, and Craft Sticks. Make six rows, and list each animal in the animal column. See Session 2.5, p. 85 for an example.

</td></tr>
</table>

☑ Checklist Available

Measuring with Kid Steps

Math Focus Points

◆ Measuring length by iterating a single unit

◆ Measuring lengths using different-sized units

◆ Comparing lengths to determine which is longer

Vocabulary

distance

Today's Plan		Materials
① ACTIVITY **Measuring in Kid Steps** 45 MIN CLASS PAIRS		• *Student Activity Book*, pp. 16–17 • Lengths of tape*
② DISCUSSION **Which Is Farther?** 15 MIN CLASS		• *Student Activity Book*, pp. 16–17 • Measuring tape, ruler, and yardstick
③ SESSION FOLLOW-UP **Daily Practice and Homework**		• *Student Activity Book*, pp. 18–19 • *Student Math Handbook*, pp. 103, 105

*See *Materials to Prepare*, p. 59.

Classroom Routines

Start With/Get To: Forward or Backward? Choose both the *start with* and *get to* numbers from a single basket holding the numbers 1 to 60. Ask students to find and mark both numbers on the 100 chart. Decide as a class if you will be counting forward or backward (up or down). As a class, count from the *start with* number to the *get to* number.

ACTIVITY

1 Measuring in Kid Steps

45 MIN   CLASS   PAIRS

Begin this activity by showing students the eight different tapes that you placed around the room.

I've put tape on the floor to show different distances, or paths, between things. The tape that has an *A* on it shows how far it is from [Jacob's desk to the door], and the one that has a *B* on it shows how far from [my desk to the door]. Do you think it's farther from [my desk to the door] or from [Jacob's desk to the door]?

Ask students for their predictions and talk about the reasons for them. Then ask students for ways that they could test their predictions.

How could we know for sure whether it's farther from [my desk to the door] or from [Jacob's desk to the door]?

Students might say:

"You could measure them with cubes."

"You could put tiles on them and count them and find out which has more."

You could use cubes, and I bet there would be quite a few of them! It would take a long time to put them together and count all of them. When people have something longer to measure, like we have today, they usually use longer units. Sometimes adults use their feet to measure how long something is. Have you ever seen adults do this?

Let's try measuring Tape A with our steps to see how it works. We're going to use *kid steps*. Sometimes people call these baby steps, but you're not babies, so we'll call them kid steps.

Ask for a volunteer to come up and measure one of the tapes you have laid out, using his or her feet.

Professional Development

❶ Teacher Note: Talking About Partial Units, p. 89

❷ Dialogue Box: More Measuring with Partial Units, p. 99

Name _____ Date _____

Fish Lengths and Animal Jumps

Distances in the Classroom (page 1 of 2)

Measure the tapes by using kid steps, and find out which is longer.

1. How long is Tape A? _____ kid steps

   How long is Tape B? _____ kid steps

   Which is longer?   Tape A   Tape B

2. How long is Tape C? _____ kid steps

   How long is Tape D? _____ kid steps

   Which is longer?   Tape C   Tape D

3. How long is Tape E? _____ kid steps

   How long is Tape F? _____ kid steps

   Which is longer?   Tape E   Tape F

4. How long is Tape G? _____ kid steps

   How long is Tape H? _____ kid steps

   Which is longer?   Tape G   Tape H

16 Unit 5   Session 2.1

© Pearson Education 1

▲ **Student Activity Book, p. 16**

We want to measure Tape A, which is the distance from [my desk to the door]. [Stacy] is going to be our measurer and she's going to measure this distance by putting one foot in front of the other, toe-to-heel like this. (Demonstrate briefly.) Where should she put her foot to start? What should she do next?

Establish with students that the *start* involves lining up the person's heel with the start of the tape. The heel of the other foot is placed at the toe of the starting foot, and the person continues walking, heel to toe. Be sure to keep track of the count as the volunteer walks the length of the tape. As the volunteer gets near the end, ask students where he or she should stop and how to count this final step.

It looks like [Stacy's] last step is too big—it goes past the end of the tape. 15 kid steps isn't enough to get to the end of the tape, but 16 is too much. How many steps should we say it is?

Drawing from their experiences in Investigation 1, students will probably suggest calling this distance *between 15 and 16*, or *a little more than 15*. Record these suggestions on the board, and talk about the different ways of representing this distance.❶ ❷

We've talked about how to measure in kid steps, but we still don't know which is longer—the distance from [my desk to the door] or the distance from [Jacob's desk to the door]. You are going to work with a partner and compare the lengths of Tape A and Tape B so that you can answer the question for yourselves. You'll also compare some other distances in the classroom to see which are longer.

Have students turn to *Student Activity Book* pages 16 and 17.

You and your partner will each get to measure and compare some of these tapes, using kid steps. You will record your work on *Student Activity Book* pages 16 and 17. On the first page, you will measure and record the length of two tapes and say which is longer. You will do this four times. Then you will choose any two tapes to compare and say which is longer.

Each of you needs to do this on your own sheet, using your own steps. Your partner will help you keep track of the number of steps while you measure. Take turns being the measurer and the helper. No more than four people can be working on the same tape at the same time.

As students work on this activity, monitor the number of pairs measuring any given tape and suggest different comparisons that students might work on if bottlenecks arise.

ONGOING ASSESSMENT: Observing Students at Work

Students measure and compare longer lengths.

- **Are students aligning their heels with the beginning of the tape and carefully putting their heels in front of their toes as they measure?**

- **Are students accurately counting and keeping track of the number of kid steps?**

- **How do students show lengths that are in between whole numbers of kid steps?**

- **Are students double-checking when they are not sure of their measurements?**

- **Do students record their own measurements on their own *Student Activity Book*, or are they mixing up their measurements with those of their partner?**

DIFFERENTIATION: Supporting the Range of Learners

Intervention Students may experience different kinds of challenges with this task. Those who have problems with motor skills in pacing may want to use a yardstick to help them keep their balance. (Students who cannot pace may use hands—heel to fingertip—to measure or may place a pair of shoes alternately along the strip. Those who are having difficulty keeping track of kid steps while they measure may need to count aloud with their partner. Many students will have difficulty measuring the last step of the tape. You may want to help them mark the next-to-final step in pencil on the tape itself and discuss how long the remaining piece of tape is. This provides a concrete image of how long the *remainder* is and allows students to consider it carefully.

Extension Some students may be interested in determining how much longer one tape is than another.

ELL Some English Language Learners might be confused by the way the words *long/longer* and *far/farther* are used interchangeably in this activity. You can emphasize the relationship between these terms as you observe the students' work. Libby and Sacha are measuring *how long* Tape A is. This will tell us *how far* it is from [Javier's desk to the door]. Teo and William are measuring *how long* Tape B is. This will tell us *how far* it is from [my desk to the door]. Which tape do you think is *longer*—Tape A or Tape B? So which distance do you think is *farther*—the distance from [Javier's desk to the door] or the distance from [my desk to the door]?

Name _____ Date _____

Fish Lengths and Animal Jumps

Distances in the Classroom (page 2 of 2)

Choose two tapes you have not compared yet.
Record which is longer.

5. Tape _____ is _____ kid steps long.

   Tape _____ is _____ kid steps long.

   Which tape is longer? _____

6. Tape _____ is _____ kid steps long.

   Tape _____ is _____ kid steps long.

   Which tape is longer? _____

Session 2.1   Unit 5 17

▲ **Student Activity Book, p. 17**

2 Which Is Farther?

15 MIN   CLASS

Math Focus Points for Discussion

◆ Comparing lengths to determine which is longer

Gather the class together for a discussion of their work. Students will need *Student Activity Book* pages 16–17. Not all of the measurements will be completed, but students should have done at least two comparisons, which entail four measurements.

Today we measured lengths in the classroom with kid steps. One of the first questions I asked was, "Is it farther from [my desk to the door] or from [Jacob's desk to the door]?" Many of you measured these two lengths, Tape A and Tape B. Which one was farther?

Ask students to check their pages and find these numbers. Then ask for a show of hands concerning which distance was greater. Do a quick tally of the results.

Do the same for the other three comparisons on the list, each time asking students which distance was greater. At some point in the discussion, students are likely to state their numerical measurements. You will return to this information in Session 2.2, but at this point in the discussion, the idea is to establish which distance is greater.

If there is disagreement about which distance of a pair is longer, ask a volunteer to pace each length while the others count the kid steps aloud. Students should agree about which distance is greater for each of the pairs of measurements.

Before the end of the session, ask students whether they have ever noticed the measuring tools adults sometimes use. Show students a measuring tape, a ruler, and a yardstick, and tell them that these are frequently used to measure length.

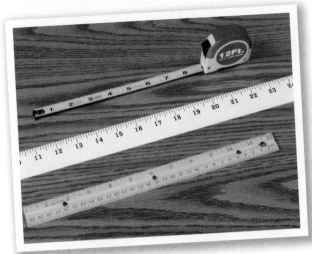

Students consider different tools for measuring length.

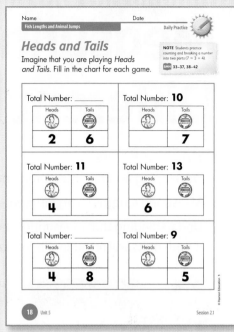

▲ Student Activity Book, p. 18

SESSION FOLLOW-UP

Daily Practice and Homework

 Daily Practice: For ongoing review, have students complete *Student Activity Book* page 18.

Homework: Explain that students will be using the same measuring procedure to see how far it is from one place to another at home. Tell students to record their answers on *Student Activity Book* page 19.

At home, you don't have pieces of tape on the floor to show how far it is from one place to another, but you can still measure in kid steps. Let's say that you were measuring from the stove to the sink—where would you start and where would you stop?

 Student Math Handbook: Students and families may use *Student Math Handbook* pages 103, 105 for reference and review. See pages 101–104 in the back of this unit. Answer students' questions about procedures.

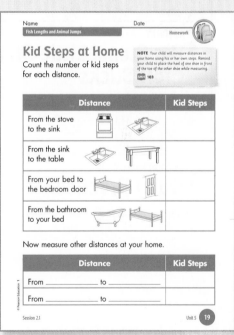

▲ Student Activity Book, p. 19

Measuring with Different Units

Math Focus Points

◆ Developing accurate measurement techniques

◆ Measuring lengths using different-sized units

◆ Understanding that measuring an object using different-length units will result in different measurements

Today's Plan		Materials
DISCUSSION **①Our Different Results**	15 MIN CLASS	• *Student Activity Book*, pp. 16–17 (from Session 2.1) • Lengths of tape (from Session 2.1)
ACTIVITY **②Big Steps, Little Steps, and Craft Sticks**	45 MIN PAIRS INDIVIDUALS	• *Student Activity Book*, p. 21 • M29 ☑ (from Session 1.6), M33* • Lengths of tape (from Session 2.1); craft sticks; envelopes of baby steps*; envelopes of basketball player steps*; 8 sheets of chart paper (1 per strip of tape); markers
SESSION FOLLOW-UP **③Daily Practice**		• *Student Activity Book*, p. 22 • *Student Math Handbook*, pp. 96–98, 103

*See *Materials to Prepare,* p. 59.

Classroom Routines

Start With/Get To: Forward or Backward? Choose both the *start with* and *get to* numbers from a basket holding the numbers 1 to 60. Ask students to find and mark both numbers on the 100 chart. Decide as a class if you will be counting forward or backward (up or down). As a class, count from the *start with* number to the *get to* number.

DISCUSSION
1 Our Different Results

15 MIN   CLASS

Math Focus Points for Discussion

◆ Understanding that measuring an object using different-length units will result in different measurements

Gather the class together to continue discussion of their work in the previous session. They need *Student Activity Book* pages 16–17.

Yesterday we measured distances in the classroom with kid steps and talked about whether it is farther from the door to [my desk] or to [Jacob's desk]. Today we'll look at how many kid steps these distances are.

Ask several students to report the numbers of kid steps they measured from [your desk to the door] and from [Jacob's desk to the door]. Record these numbers on the chart for the appropriate tape and label the numbers "Kid Steps." Because children's feet differ in size, there will no doubt be differences. Ask students about the differences.

When we measured things before, we expected to get the same answer for the same object. This time, we got all kinds of different numbers. Why did that happen?

Students might say:

"My feet are bigger than Diego's feet."

"Our feet are all different."

Most students will not be able to say *how* the size of the foot relates to the number of steps taken, and it is not important to discuss this now. The important idea is that using different-length units will result in different numbers.❶

Professional Development

❶ **Dialogue Box:** More Steps or Fewer?, p. 100

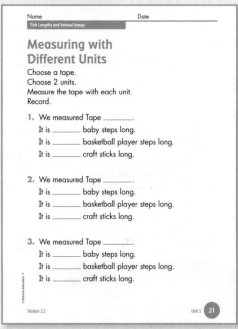

Name	Date

Fish Lengths and Animal Jumps

Measuring with Different Units

Choose a tape.
Choose 2 units.
Measure the tape with each unit.
Record.

1. We measured Tape _____.
   It is _____ baby steps long.
   It is _____ basketball player steps long.
   It is _____ craft sticks long.

2. We measured Tape _____.
   It is _____ baby steps long.
   It is _____ basketball player steps long.
   It is _____ craft sticks long.

3. We measured Tape _____.
   It is _____ baby steps long.
   It is _____ basketball player steps long.
   It is _____ craft sticks long.

Session 2.2   Unit 5   21

▲ **Student Activity Book, p. 21;**
Resource Masters, M33

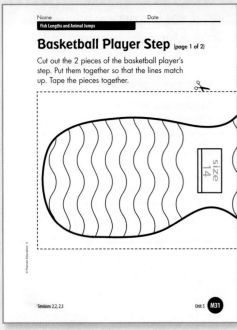

▲ Resource Masters, M31

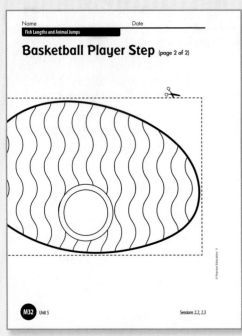

▲ Resource Masters, M32

After students have shared their ideas and identified that the size of the foot might be important, ask for a volunteer who has small feet to come forward. Choose a line of tape that everyone can see, and ask the volunteer to pace this line while everyone counts. Record this person's measurement on the chart.

[Tamika] counted [17] kid steps when she measured this line. Now let's have someone who has bigger feet come up and measure the line.

After the second volunteer paces, record this measurement as well and ask students to compare the two numbers.

[Paul] took [15] kid steps to measure the line. We know that [Tamika] and [Paul] were very careful about how they measured. Some of you said that the size of a person's foot might lead to different measurements. You may be right! We're going to find out more about this during Math Workshop.

45 MIN | PAIRS | INDIVIDUALS

ACTIVITY

② Big Steps, Little Steps, and Craft Sticks

Students will work with three different units to measure various tapes. They will continue work on this activity tomorrow. Have students turn to *Student Activity Book* page 21.

For this activity, you'll be measuring some of the same tapes you measured yesterday. Today, you will use different units: steps of a baby, steps of a basketball player, and craft sticks. Let's start by thinking about how to measure with craft sticks.

Let's say that I want to measure this tape with craft sticks. (Use one of the tapes on the floor that everyone can see.) How should we line them up when we measure?

Demonstrate, or ask a volunteer to demonstrate, measuring with the sticks. Point out to students that the sticks are in a straight line from beginning to end with no gaps or overlaps. Let students know that they will be comparing their measurements, so they need to be careful about how they measure.

Now, hold up a baby step cut from Baby Steps (M30), and tell students that this is an outline of a real baby's foot one month after her birth.

On the tables are some envelopes labeled Baby Steps. When you measure the steps, remember to line them up heel to toe just like we did with our own steps.

Now, hold up Basketball Player Step (M31–M32) and tell students this is an outline of a size 14 sneaker worn by a basketball player.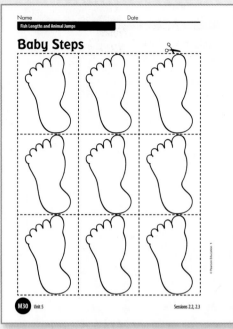

This basketball player's foot is much longer than the baby's foot and even much longer than our own steps!

Ask students to look at the recording sheet, and show them that for each tape they measure, they need to record what unit they use and how long the tape is.

Next, show students the eight charts, one for each length of tape. Tell students that they will put each of their measurements on the charts.

Let's say that you measured Tape F with baby steps. When you've finished measuring, write the number of baby steps on the "Tape F" chart so that we have a class record of it. Record each measurement that you make. Remember, you must write down the unit you used and the number. We'll have a few different measurements up there on each chart, because different people will be measuring the same tapes.

During workshop time, be sure to measure at least two tapes with craft sticks, two tapes with baby steps, and two tapes with basketball player steps. If you complete *Student Activity Book* page 21, I will give you a copy of Measuring with Different Units (M33) and you can measure more tapes. You'll work on this today and tomorrow.

Students learn that different units yield different measurements.

▲ **Resource Masters, M30**

Teaching Note

❷ **Iterating Units** It is likely that students will not have enough baby and basketball steps to measure these lengths. Encourage students to think about how they can use the steps they have to measure the distance by iterating a single unit or by laying out the units, counting them, and moving them along the length of the tape.

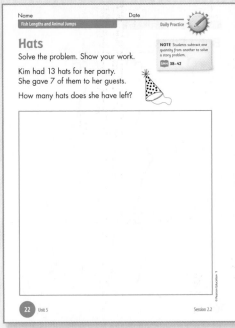

Name _____ Date _____

Fish Lengths and Animal Jumps   Daily Practice

Hats

Solve the problem. Show your work.

NOTE Students subtract one quantity from another to solve a story problem.

SMH 38–42

Kim had 13 hats for her party.
She gave 7 of them to her guests.

How many hats does she have left?

22   Unit 5   Session 2.2

▲ **Student Activity Book, p. 22**

As students work, once again make sure that they are distributed fairly equally among the tapes on the floor (no more than two pairs per tape). Remind students that they need to record their measurements on *Student Activity Book* page 21 as well as on the charts.

During this activity, as well as during Animal Jumps in Sessions 2.4 and 2.5, you will continue to assess each of your students' measuring techniques. Continue to use Assessment Checklist: Measurement Techniques (M29). For an illustration of one teacher's chart, see Session 1.6. For the assessment, ask each child to measure a distance on his or her own.

ONGOING ASSESSMENT: Observing Students at Work

As students work, look for the following:

- **Are students demonstrating appropriate measurement techniques?**

- **Are students keeping track of their counts, particularly when a large number of units is involved?**

- **How do students handle in-between measurements, in which a fractional part is involved?** Do they know how to count the basketball player steps?

- **Do students record the unit of measurement they are using, or do they simply write numbers without regard to the unit?**

SESSION FOLLOW-UP

3 Daily Practice

Daily Practice: For ongoing review, have students complete *Student Activity Book* page 22.

Student Math Handbook: Students and families may use *Student Math Handbook* pages 96–98, 103 for reference and review. See pages 101–104 in the back of this unit.

Measuring with Different Units, *continued*

Math Focus Points

◆ Describing measurements that are *in between* whole numbers of units

◆ Measuring lengths using different-sized ~~units~~

◆ Comparing lengths to determine which is longer

◆ ~~Under~~standing that measuring an object using different-~~sized u~~nits will result in different measurements

Vocabulary

in between

Today's Plan

ACTIVITY
① Big Steps, Little Craft Sticks

ACTIVITY
② What Did We Find

🕐 👥
20 MIN GROUPS

DISCUSSION
③ Different Units, Different Counts

🕐 👥
15 MIN CLASS

SESSION FOLLOW-UP
④ Daily Practice

Materials

• *Student Activity Book*, p. 21 (from Session 2.2)
• M29 ☑ (from Session 1.6), M33
• Envelopes containing baby steps; basketball player steps; lengths of tape; craft sticks; partially completed charts (from Session 2.2); markers

• *Student Activity Book*, p. 23
• Completed charts (from Activity 1)

• *Student Activity Book*, p. 23

• *Student Activity Book*, p. 24
• *Student Math Handbook*, pp. 96, 100–103

Classroom Routines

Quick Images: Coins Using the set of overhead coins, display 2 pennies and 2 dimes in groups of two. Follow the basic *Quick Images* activity. Ask questions that focus on identifying each coin and the total number of coins (e.g. Which coin is the [dime]? How are these coins similar? What is the name of *this* coin? How many coins did you see? How do you know?). If time permits, repeat using 3 nickels and 3 quarters.

ACTIVITY

Big Steps, Little Steps, and Craft Sticks

25 MIN PAIRS

For complete details about this activity, see Session 2.2, pages 70–72. If students measure three tapes and finish *Student Activity Book* page 21, give them a copy of Measuring with Different Units (M33) so that they can measure more tapes.

Continue to use the Assessment Checklist: Measurement Techniques (M29) during this activity to assess each of your students' measuring techniques.

Students can use craft sticks to measure objects.

ONGOING ASSESSMENT: Observing Students at Work

As students work, look for the following:

- **Are students demonstrating appropriate measurement techniques?**

- **Are students keeping track of their counts, particularly when a large number of units is involved?**

- **How do students handle in-between measurements, in which a fractional part is involved?** Do they know how to count the basketball player steps?

- **Do students record the unit of measurement they are using, or do they simply write numbers without regard to the type of unit?**

ACTIVITY

2 What Did We Find?

20 MIN GROUPS

As students wrap up their work with measuring the tapes, remind them to record their measurements on the sheets of chart paper. Then gather them together and explain the next task.

You are going to work in groups and make a report to the class on some of our measurements. Each group will get one chart with all the measurements for one of the tapes on it. You need to look at the measurements on your chart and figure out these things:

- What did you need the most of when measuring: the baby steps, craft sticks, or the basketball player's steps?

- What did you need the fewest of to measure?

- Why do you think you needed so many of one kind of unit and so few of the other kind of unit to measure the same thing?

You will record your information on *Student Activity Book* page 23.

Assign students to groups. Answer questions about what they are to do. Each group should have a recorder write *notes* or a few words to help them remember what they want to say to the class.

Give each group a completed chart, and have them work for about 15 minutes to prepare their reports by filling in *Student Activity Book* page 23.

Working in groups helps students learn from one another.

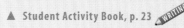

Name _____ **Date** _____

Fish Lengths and Animal Jumps

Reporting What We Found 🖊

1. What tape do you have? Tape _____

2. Which measurement of the tape used the <u>greatest</u> number of units?

    Baby steps   Basketball player steps   Craft sticks

3. Which measurement of the tape used the <u>least</u> number of units?

    Baby steps   Basketball player steps   Craft sticks

4. Why were the numbers different?

Session 2.3   Unit 5 **23**

▲ **Student Activity Book, p. 23**

ONGOING ASSESSMENT: Observing Students at Work

Students analyze footstep data as a way of thinking about the relationship between the size of the unit and the length of the measurement.

- **How do students make sense of the numbers?** Are they able to identify baby steps as needing the greatest number of units to measure? Do they identify the basketball player's steps as needing the fewest number of units to measure?

- **How do students explain their findings?** Do they understand that different sizes mean different amounts? Do they understand that the larger the unit, the fewer of them are needed to measure a given length?

- **If there are very different measurements of the same tape, made with the same unit, do students notice it and draw the conclusion that at least one of the measurements must be inaccurate?**

DIFFERENTIATION: Supporting the Range of Learners

ELL In the previous activity, students used comparatives such as *long/longer* and *far/farther*. In this activity, they must use the superlatives *most, least,* and *fewest,* which were introduced in Unit 2. (See Unit 2 Overview.) If necessary, you can review these terms with English Language Learners before beginning this activity.

15 MIN   CLASS

DISCUSSION

Different Units, Different Counts

Math Focus Points for Discussion

◆ Understanding that measuring an object using different-length units will result in different measurements

Have each group identify their tape and say what they found. As groups are reporting, point out the similarities in what they discovered, and ask students to look for patterns as well.

We've heard reports about Tape [A, B, and C]. So far, all of the groups have said that *baby steps* needed the most number of units to measure, that *basketball player steps* took the fewest units to measure. Do you think this will keep happening for the other tapes? Why or why not?

Students might say:

"Baby steps are really small so you need lots of them to fill a distance."

"Basketball players have lots bigger feet than babies. It would only take them a few steps."

This is an idea they will work on more in second grade. In first grade, it is enough that students realize that units of different size result in different counts when measuring the same distance. ❶

SESSION FOLLOW-UP
4 Daily Practice

Daily Practice: For ongoing review, have students complete *Student Activity Book* page 24.

Student Math Handbook: Students and families may use *Student Math Handbook* pages 96, 100–103 for reference and review. See pages 101–104 in the back of this unit.

Teaching Note

❶ **Preparation** Before Session 2.4, remember to take away the tapes measured in Sessions 2.2 and 2.3 and prepare new tapes for use in the next session.

Name ___ Date ___

Fish Lengths and Animal Jumps   Daily Practice

How Many Snowballs?

NOTE Students combine two quantities to solve a story problem.
SMH 33–37

Solve the problem. Show your work.

Rosa made 8 snowballs.
Max also made 8 snowballs.

How many snowballs did they make?

24 Unit 5   Session 2.3

▲ Student Activity Book, p. 24

Measuring Jumps

Math Focus Points

◈ Developing accurate measurement techniques

◈ Solving problems about comparing lengths

Vocabulary

longest
shortest

Today's Plan		Materials
1 ACTIVITY **Introducing Animal Jumps**	15 MIN CLASS	• *Student Activity Book*, pp. 25–27 • Yardstick; Animal Jump Tapes*

2 MATH WORKSHOP
Measuring Jumps
2A Animal Jumps
2B Jumping Story Problems
	45 MIN	**2A** • *Student Activity Book*, p. 25
		 • M29 ☑ (from Session 1.6)
		 • Animal Jump Tapes*; envelopes
		   containing baby steps
		   (from Session 2.2); craft sticks
		2B • *Student Activity Book*, pp. 26–27
		   (from Activity 1)
		 • Counters

3 SESSION FOLLOW-UP **Daily Practice**		• *Student Activity Book*, p. 28 • *Student Math Handbook*, pp. 100–101, 104–106

*See *Materials to Prepare,* p. 61.

Classroom Routines

Quick Survey: Sneakers? On chart paper, create a 2-column table entitled "Are You Wearing Sneakers" with the headings "Yes" and "No" at the top of the table. Use tally marks to record the students' responses and then count them by fives and ones. After counting the responses, have a short discussion about the results of the survey.

ACTIVITY

1 Introducing Animal Jumps

15 MIN   CLASS

Begin the activity by spending a few minutes identifying animals that are good at jumping (including grasshoppers, horses, kangaroos, squirrels, frogs, and some kinds of spiders). You might want to give some examples of jumping feats, such as the following:❶

- Jumping field mice can jump as far as a yardstick (show how long that is) when they are suddenly scared.

- Grasshoppers can jump up to 20 times the length of their own bodies.

- Frogs are such good jumpers that some people have frog jumping contests.

- Kangaroos can jump as far as 40 feet, as long as a school bus.

During Math Workshop, you'll measure how far different animals—including first graders—can jump. You can choose to use baby steps or craft sticks as a measuring unit, but whichever you choose, you need to measure all of the jumps with that unit.

In these two sections of the room, I've put down tapes showing how far different animals jump. The animals are a squirrel, a rabbit, a field mouse, a frog, a grasshopper, and a $6\frac{1}{2}$ year-old named Max. The names are on the tapes. You will work on this activity by yourself to find out which animal has the longest jump and which one has the shortest.

Read *Student Activity Book* page 25 aloud and explain to students that they will use this sheet to record their measurements during the first Math Workshop activity.

Introduce the second Math Workshop activity. Explain that students will solve the problems on *Student Activity Book* pages 26 and 27. Read over each problem with students.❷ Call students' attention to the class number line and the counters, which they may want to use as they work on the problems. Remind students that when they work in pairs on these problems, one student reads the problem aloud while the other closes his or her eyes to visualize what the problem is about. They should talk about what the problem says and what it is asking before solving the problem.

Name _____ Date _____

Fish Lengths and Animal Jumps

Animal Jumps

What unit did you use to measure? (Circle one)

    Baby steps   Craft sticks

1. The rabbit's jump was _____ units long.
2. The frog's jump was _____ units long.
3. The mouse's jump was _____ units long.
4. Max's jump was _____ units long.
5. The squirrel's jump was _____ units long.
6. The grasshopper's jump was _____ units long.

List the animal names in order by how long their jumps were.

Longest _____

Next longest _____

Next longest _____

Next longest _____

Next longest _____

Shortest _____

Session 2.4   Unit 5 **25**

▲ **Student Activity Book, p. 25**

Teaching Notes

❶ **Explanation** Good jumpers typically have strong back legs that they use to push off.

❷ **Reading Story Problems** Depending on the reading level of your students you will need to make a decision about how to support them in this activity.

Student Activity Book, p. 26

Name _____ Date _____

Fish Lengths and Animal Jumps

Jumping Word Problems (page 1 of 2)

Solve each problem. Show your work.

1. Sam's cat jumped 6 craft sticks. Rosa's cat jumped 3 craft sticks. Which cat jumped farther? How much farther did it jump?

2. A rabbit jumped 8 basketball player steps. Then it jumped 5 basketball player steps. How far did it jump in all?

3. Kim jumped 8 craft sticks. Max jumped 10 craft sticks. How much farther did Max jump than Kim?

26   Unit 5   Session 2.4

▲ **Student Activity Book, p. 26**

Name _____ Date _____

Fish Lengths and Animal Jumps

Jumping Word Problems (page 2 of 2)

4. Sam jumped 2 basketball player steps. Then he jumped 3 basketball player steps. Then he jumped 4 basketball player steps. How far did he jump in all?

5. A frog jumped to the pond. It jumped 4 kid steps. Then it jumped 6 kid steps. How many kid steps did the frog jump?

6. A squirrel jumped 6 craft sticks. A rabbit jumped 9 craft sticks. How much farther did the rabbit jump than the squirrel?

Session 2.4   Unit 5   27

▲ **Student Activity Book, p. 27**

MATH WORKSHOP

2 Measuring Jumps

45 MIN

Students work on two activities that involve measuring and comparing jumps.

. . . .

2A Animal Jumps

INDIVIDUALS

Continue to use Assessment Checklist: Measurement Techniques (M29) during this activity for those students whose measurement techniques were not assessed in Sessions 2.2 or 2.3.

ONGOING ASSESSMENT: Observing Students at Work

This activity offers another opportunity to observe and assess students' measurement techniques.

- **Do students understand that they need to choose and stick with one unit in order to compare the different animal jumps, or do they measure different jumps with different units?**

- **Are students lining up the units in a straight line without gaps or overlaps?**

- **Are they able to count and keep track of the units and record measurements accurately?** How do they record partial units?

- **On *Student Activity Book* page 25, are students able to put their measurements in order by size from longest to shortest?**

. . . .

2B Jumping Story Problems

PAIRS

Students work in pairs on a set of word problems.

ONGOING ASSESSMENT: Observing Students at Work

This set of word problems involves either combining or comparing lengths of jumps.

- **Are students able to read the problem and visualize the situation?**

- **Are students able to identify these problems as combining two amounts or comparing two lengths to see which is more?** Can they determine the difference?

- **What strategies do students use to combine these two quantities?** Do they combine both groups and count all? Count on from one number? Use a known number combination?

- **What strategies do students use to compare two lengths?** Do they model the problem with counters and directly compare? Do they count on or back from one number? Do they use a number relationship? Do they use counters or a number line?

DIFFERENTIATION: Supporting the Range of Learners

Intervention Because the set of problems contains stories about combining jumps and about comparing jumps, some students may need to be reminded to read the problems carefully to make sure that they can visualize each story. Some students may benefit from acting out the problem with the units in the story (e.g., craft sticks, basketball player steps). Comparison problems such as Problems 1, 3, and 6 are challenging for first graders, even though the numbers involved in these problems are small. Encourage students to model the problems as well.

Extension If students are easily able to solve the jumping story problem and explain their strategies, give them a new set of problems with bigger numbers.

SESSION FOLLOW-UP

3 Daily Practice

Daily Practice: For ongoing review, have students complete *Student Activity Book* page 28.

Student Math Handbook: Students and families may use *Student Math Handbook* pages 100–101, 104–106 for reference and review. See pages 101–104 in the back of this unit.

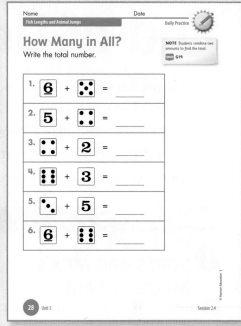

▲ Student Activity Book, p. 28

End-of-Unit Assessment

Math Focus Points

◆ Understanding that measuring an object using different-length units will result in different measurements

◆ Developing accurate measurement techniques

◆ Solving problems about comparing length

Vocabulary

measurement
unit

Today's Plan		Materials
ASSESSMENT ACTIVITY ❶ **Sam's and Max's Measurements**	✓ 🕐 👤 15 MIN INDIVIDUALS	• M34*
MATH WORKSHOP ❷ **Animal Jumps** ❷Ⓐ Animal Jumps ❷Ⓑ Jumping Story Problems	🕐 30 MIN	❷Ⓐ • *Student Activity Book*, p. 25 (from Session 2.4) • M29 ☑ (from Session 1.6) ❷Ⓑ • *Student Activity Book*, pp. 26–27 • Counters
DISCUSSION ❸ **Jumping Distances**	🕐 👥 15 MIN CLASS	• *Student Activity Book*, p. 25 (from Session 2.4) • Animal Jumps chart* • Number line
SESSION FOLLOW-UP ❹ **Daily Practice**		• *Student Activity Book*, p. 29 • *Student Math Handbook*, pp. 96, 104–106

*See *Materials to Prepare*, p. 61.

Classroom Routines

Start With/Get To: Forward or Backward? **Choose both the *start with* and *get to* numbers from a basket holding the numbers 1 to 60. Ask students to find and mark both numbers on the 100 chart. Decide as a class if you will be counting forward or backward (up or down). As a class, count from the *start with* number to the *get to* number.**

1 ASSESSMENT ACTIVITY
Sam's and Max's Measurements

15 MIN INDIVIDUALS

Introduce this assessment problem by reading aloud the problem on End-of-Unit Assessment (M34). Explain to students that you would like them to work alone so that you can get an idea about how they are thinking about measurement. ❶

Problem 1 should help you assess if students understand that measuring with different-sized units will give different counts (Benchmark 4).

ONGOING ASSESSMENT: Observing Students at Work

The End-of-Unit Assessment question provides information about the following:

- **Do students understand that when measuring the same object, different-sized units yield different counts?**

2 MATH WORKSHOP
Animal Jumps

30 MIN

As students finish the assessment, they continue with the two Math Workshop activities from the previous session.

2A Animal Jumps

INDIVIDUALS

For complete details about this activity, see Session 2.4, pages 79–80. This will be your final opportunity to assess individual students' measuring techniques with Assessment Checklist (M29).

Name _____ Date _____

Fish Lengths and Animal Jumps

End-of-Unit Assessment

Rosa jumped as far as she could. Sam measured Rosa's jump heel-to-toe with kid steps.

Max measured Rosa's jump with craft sticks. Sam and Max got different numbers.

1. Can Sam and Max both be right?

2. Why did they get different numbers for their measurements?

M34 Unit 5   Session 2.5

▲ Resource Masters, M34

Professional Development

❶ **Teacher Note:** End-of-Unit Assessment, p. 95

Students use different units to measure the lengths of animal jumps.

2B Jumping Story Problems

PAIRS

For complete details about this activity, see Session 2.4, pages 80–81.

DISCUSSION

3 Jumping Distances

15 MIN   CLASS

Math Focus Points for Discussion

◆ Understanding that measuring an object using different-length units will result in different measurements

◆ Solving problems about comparing lengths

Gather students together with *Student Activity Book* page 25 to compare the jumps of various animals.

Begin the discussion by asking students to share the measurements they got for the different animals. Record these on the Animal Jumps chart you have prepared.

Animal Jumps

Animal	Baby Steps	Craft Sticks
Frog		
Rosa		
Jumping mouse		
Grasshopper		
Squirrel		
Rabbit		

Teaching Note

❷ **Comparison Problems in Grade Two**
Comparison problems will next arise in second grade, again in the context of measurement. In third grade, comparison problems will become a major emphasis in *Trading Stickers, Combining Coins.*

Review the idea that if students used the same unit to measure the same jump, they should get the same measurement; if they used different units, then they should get different counts. Ask these questions:

If everyone used the same unit to measure the frog jump, should they have gotten the same measurement? Why or why not? What if they used different units to measure?

Then ask students to think about why they can't compare jumps by looking at only the numbers.

Why can't we compare a length of 10 craft sticks with a length of 15 baby steps?

Do at least one comparison problem with the class. To do this, use a comparison of jumps that are close together and have relatively small numbers, such as the rabbit and frog jumps.❷

[Tamika] found that the rabbit jump was 8 craft sticks long and the frog jump was 10 craft sticks. Which jumped farther? How much farther did the frog jump than the rabbit?

Ask students to share their strategies for comparing 8 and 10 and determining the difference.

You may want to draw and label these lengths on the board. Point out that the two main strategies (counting on and counting back) result in the same answer. Use the number line to illustrate each strategy.

[William] thought about the problem by going back from 10 craft sticks—the frog jump—to 8 craft sticks—the rabbit jump. He did it on the number line.

Teaching Note

❸ Measurement in Grade Two In Grade 2, students will continue to develop their measurement techniques with greater emphasis on inches, feet, centimeters, and meters. They will learn to use rulers, and they will return to the idea that when measuring a single length with different units, the larger unit will yield a smaller count.

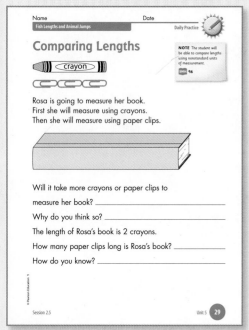

▲ Student Activity Book, p. 29

[Tamika] also used the number line, but she added on to go from 8 craft sticks (the rabbit jump) to 10 craft sticks (the frog jump).

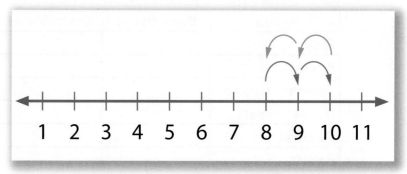

Close the discussion by telling students that this is the end of the measurement unit but that you expect there will be many situations coming up when they will find it useful to measure. ❸

SESSION FOLLOW-UP

4 Daily Practice

Daily Practice: For enrichment, have students complete *Student Activity Book* page 29.

Student Math Handbook: Students and families may use *Student Math Handbook* pages 96, 104–106 for reference and review. See pages 101–104 in the back of this unit.

Fish Lengths and Animal Jumps

In Part 6 of *Implementing Investigations in Grade 1,* you will find a set of Teacher Notes that addresses topics and issues applicable to the curriculum as a whole rather than to specific curriculum units. They include the following:

Computational Fluency and Place Value

Computational Algorithms and Methods

Representations and Contexts for Mathematical Work

Foundations of Algebra in the Elementary Grades

Discussing Mathematical Ideas

**Racial and Linguistic Diversity in the Classroom:
 What Does Equity Mean in Today's Math Classroom?**

Learning About Length

Students' ideas about length develop as they compare sizes of things in their everyday life:

"My sister is taller than I am."

"My pencil is the shortest one in the class."

Research on children's mathematical understanding shows that students typically do not develop a firm idea about length as a stable, measurable dimension until second grade, although, of course, there is quite a range of individual differences among students. Through experiences with comparing and ordering lengths, students develop their understanding of what length is and how it can be described.

Students in your class may vary quite a bit in how accurately and consistently they compare the lengths of things. When they begin to measure with objects, such as with connecting cubes or foot outlines, you will probably see some who do not carefully line up these objects end-to-end as they measure, instead either overlapping them or leaving spaces between them. You may also see students who count along the length of an object with the width of a finger or with a single cube, running these along the whole length of the object as they count, but not paying much attention to whether each successive placement begins right where the previous one ended. These *mistakes* are probably not just carelessness or sloppiness; instead, these students are still figuring out what measuring is about.

Rather than simply telling students to carefully align the ends of two objects in order to compare them, or demonstrating how to measure with a tower of cubes, encourage discussion among students about different ways they are measuring.

For example:

Some people said that this book was 10 cubes long, some said 9, and some said 11. Who would like to show how you measured this book? [William] lined up 10 cubes like this. Do you think that's alright? Could it be 11 cubes? Here's a tower of 11 cubes. Could that work? Why or why not?

At times, you might show students some inaccurate ways of measuring to help them think through and articulate their own ideas. For example, spread out three cubes with big gaps along the edge of a book: one at one edge of the book, one in the middle, and one lined up with the other edge. Tell students that you measured this book and that it is 3 cubes long. Ask them whether that seems right and, if not, what you should do to get a better measurement. As students discuss and compare ways of measuring, they will gradually develop a sense of what length is and how to measure it accurately.

Students discuss and compare ways of measuring by using this inaccurate method of measuring the length of a book.

Using numbers to measure length is different from using numbers to count a discrete quantity. When students count objects, each successive counting number refers to one object. But to use numbers to measure length, students have to develop the sense of a continuous interval. One unit does not refer to one object but to an interval. For example, *1* refers to an interval of length from 0 to 1.

This is a new and difficult idea. It is important that students develop this idea through many experiences with units that they can place repeatedly and count (such as connecting cubes or their feet) so that they physically experience what length is, and develop a sense of how it extends from one point to another, and how two lengths might be compared.

Some students may be interested in using rulers. You can certainly make rulers available in the classroom, but in the early grades, students usually see the numbers on the ruler simply as marks to read without understanding much about how a ruler is used as a tool to quantify length. For example, students may align the 1 on the ruler, rather than the edge of the ruler with the edge of an object. They sometimes use the ruler backward, saying that something is 10 inches when it is actually 2 inches.

Students may also think that one kind of measuring unit is equivalent to another. For example, they will find out that something is 6 cubes long and say that the length is "6 inches." They may also think that an object that is longer than another object must be one more unit long. For example, a 7-year-old who knew that she was 4 feet tall was comparing herself with a boy in the class. He was a few inches taller, and she said, "So he's 5 feet tall."

In this unit, students use a variety of measuring tools such as connecting cubes, paper clips, and craft sticks. They also use inch tiles. Because students refer to these as inch tiles, when they measure an object with the tiles they say, "The object is _____ inches long." At this early age, students can begin to develop a feel for how big an inch is without formalizing the inch as a standard unit of measure.

As students' understanding of measurement develops over time, they begin to formulate ideas about the need for standard measuring units. On the basis of the understanding students have developed through many experiences with using nonstandard units to measure, the use of standard measuring tools becomes meaningful. The need for a standard measuring tool is among the measuring topics students investigate in the Grade 2 *Investigations* unit on measurement.

Talking About Partial Units

The idea of halves or partial units will arise naturally during the work of this unit. When students are measuring lengths by lining up several cubes, tiles, paper clips, baby steps, and other nonstandard units along an object, the measurement will not always come out even. This will lead to a discussion about which of the two numbers (e.g., 16 cubes or 17 cubes) is closer to the length of the object, and how to tell. Some students have a tendency to choose the smaller of the two numbers so as not to go beyond the length of the object being measured even if the amount is actually closer to the larger of the two numbers. Other students say $17\frac{1}{2}$ because they have placed and counted the 17th unit and then, on realizing that it is too many, call it *one half* but retain 17 as the number of whole units.

As situations like this arise, ask students to think about ways we can describe an amount between two numbers. For example, we can say, *about 17 cubes, more than 16 cubes, between 16 and 17 cubes,* and so forth. If the extra unit is in fact about half, you can introduce the language and notation for one half ($\frac{1}{2}$). Explain, for example, that 16 cubes and half a cube is written this way:

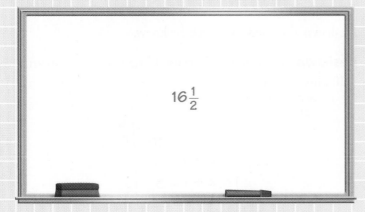

This notation will be unfamiliar to many of your students, and if they use it on their own, they may write it incorrectly. For example, many young students say 17 and a half to mean half a cube *less* than 17. Other students might reverse the numbers in the fraction and write $16\frac{2}{1}$. Although first-grade students are not expected to learn fraction notation, they can certainly begin to see it written and read correctly and begin to try it out themselves.

As second graders in the *Investigations* curriculum, students will spend more time on ideas about halves and other fractions in *How Many Floors? How Many Rooms?* (Unit 5) and *Measuring Length and Time* (Unit 9). For first graders, it is enough to recognize situations when one unit does not fit exactly into another and to have a way of talking about this.

See **Dialogue Box:** Measuring with Partial Units, page 97 and **Dialogue Box:** More Measuring with Partial Units, page 99 for more information about how students think about this issue.

Strategies to Solve Comparison Problems

First-graders are likely to present a variety of strategies for solving comparison problems like those on *Student Activity Book* pages 11 and 12 . For example, in one class, students shared their methods for solving the following problem:

Sam caught a perch that is 8 inches long. He caught an alewife that is 11 inches long. How much longer is the alewife than the perch?

As the students explained their solutions, the teacher drew a representation of each strategy.

Diego laid out 8 inch tiles to represent the perch, and 11 inch tiles to represent the alewife. Then he counted the number of tiles that the alewife extended beyond the perch.

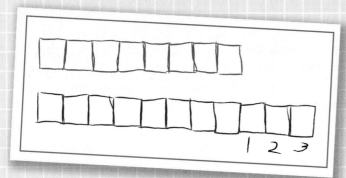

Diego's Work

Chris explained that he drew 11 tally marks. He counted 8 of them and then counted how many were left.

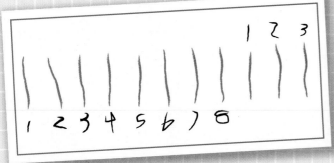

Chris's Work

Emilia remembered the problem the class had solved together the day before in which they compared a 7-inch alewife and an 11-inch mackerel.

Emilia: I knew from meeting yesterday that when there were 7 and there needed to be 4 more to get to 11, and so I knew that I could take 1 from the 4 to make 8, and then he would only need 3 more to get 11.

Emilia was answering the question in terms of how much the perch needed to grow to be as long as the alewife.

Teacher: And so how much does it need to grow?

Emilia: 3 inches.

The teacher represented Emilia's thinking:

I know that $7 + 4 = 11$
so $8 + 3 = 11$

Emilia's Work

Deshawn also used a fact that he knew.

Deshawn: It has to be 3 because I know $8 + 2 = 10$ and 10 plus 1 more is 11.

$8 + 2 = 10$
$10 + 1 = 11$
$2 + 1 = 3$

Deshawn's Work

Jacinta drew a number line to solve the problem. When the teacher represented Jacinta's method, she explained that she was going to draw in the fish to show where they could see the fish on the number line.

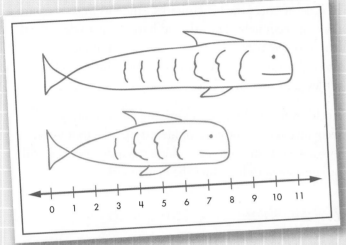

Jacinta's Work

Jacob drew 11 circles and crossed out 8 of them. Then he counted what was left and got 3.

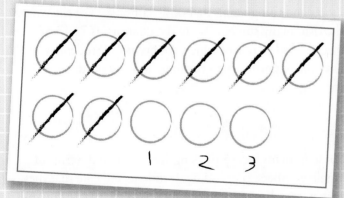

Jacob's Work

The teacher concluded the discussion by pointing out that all of the students got an answer of 3.

Teacher: It's 3 what? What question are you answering?

Deshawn: How much longer is the alewife? The alewife is 3 inches longer.

Teacher: Right. We were asked how much longer the alewife is than the perch. The alewife is 3 inches longer than the perch.

As students discussed their different strategies for comparing the measurement of the two fish, the teacher saw that many of their methods were removed from the context; their question seemed to have become how many more is 11 than 8? Some students used tally marks; some used a number line; others used numerical reasoning, relying on facts they knew. All of these are important strategies for first graders and should be encouraged.

The teacher drew the fish on Jacinta's number line for two reasons. First, it brought students back to the original context; the problem is about comparing fish. Second, it was a subtle way of showing students how length is indicated on a number line. A length of 8 extends from 0 to 8, not from 1 to 8.

In the middle of the lesson, in response to Emilia, and again at the end, the teacher asked the students what question they were answering. Again, she wanted her students to stay in touch with the problem they were solving.

Assessment: How Long Is This Fish?

Problem 1

Benchmarks addressed:

Benchmark 1: Demonstrate accurate measuring techniques when measuring a distance with nonstandard or standard units. These techniques include starting at the beginning, ending at the end, leaving no gaps or overlaps, measuring in a straight line, and keeping track of the number of units.

Benchmark 2: Know at least one way of describing a measurement that falls between two whole numbers.

In order to meet the benchmarks, students' work should show that they can:

- Measure the length of an object accurately;

- Specify a measurement between two whole units.

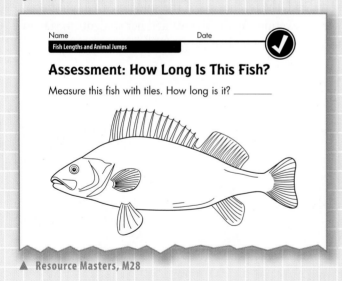

▲ Resource Masters, M28

Meeting the Benchmarks

In order to meet the benchmarks, students must measure the fish accurately. They should have a way to describe the length of the fish as between two whole numbers: between 6 and 7 tiles, a little more than 6 tiles, a little less than 7 tiles, almost 7 tiles, or 6 and $\frac{1}{2}$ tiles.

At this stage in the unit, many students will not yet recognize the importance of identifying the unit when measuring. If they do not include the unit, they can still be considered to have met the benchmark.

Partially Meeting the Benchmarks

Some students record the length as 7 and $\frac{1}{2}$. These students may have laid out the tiles correctly and realize that the length of the fish falls between two whole numbers of tiles. However, they have not yet learned how to represent a mixed numeral. After having put down 7 tiles and recognizing that only half of the last tile covers the fish, many students write the quantity as $7\frac{1}{2}$ (7 tiles placed, the last one of which counts as $\frac{1}{2}$). Students will have the opportunity to continue to work on this idea in Investigation 2.

Not Meeting the Benchmarks

Some students record the length of the fish in terms of whole numbers: 6 or 7. These students indicate that they may not yet be thinking of length as a continuous quantity that can fall between whole units. Students will have the opportunity to continue to work on this idea in Investigation 2.

The next part of the assessment refers to the same fish.

Problem 2

Benchmark addressed:

Benchmark 3: Understand that the same result should be obtained when the same object is measured twice or when two different people measure the same object (with the same unit).

In order to meet the benchmark, students' work should show that they can:

• Explain errors in measurement.

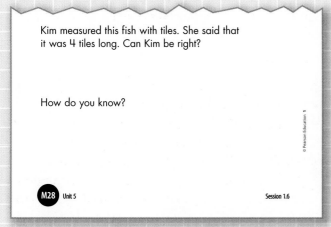

Kim measured this fish with tiles. She said that it was 4 tiles long. Can Kim be right?

How do you know?

© Pearson Education 1

M28 Unit 5   Session 1.6

▲ **Resource Masters, M28**

Meeting the Benchmark

Students who meet the benchmark indicate that Kim cannot be right and offer a valid explanation.

Allie suggested that Kim's error came from leaving spaces between tiles.

NO
BeCause She used SPACiSS BesWin The TiLes.

Allie's Work

Felipe says, "I measured it two times and it was $7\frac{1}{2}$." Although he did not represent the length of the fish correctly, he did indicate that both measurements cannot be correct, and because he got the same result twice, Kim's must be incorrect.

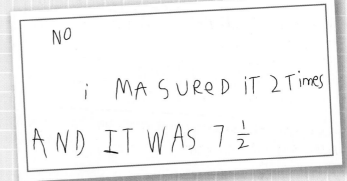

NO
i MASUReD iT 2Times AND IT WAS 7 $\frac{1}{2}$

Felipe's Work

Libby explained, "You can't use any other utensil," indicating that she is already thinking about Benchmark 4—that different-sized units result in different counts when measuring the same length.

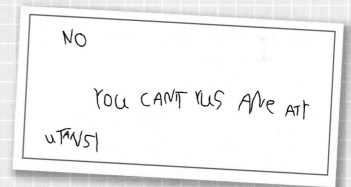

NO
You CANT Yus ANe ATr uTANSl

Libby's Work

Vic simply states, "Because I measured the fish on top." Because his measurement came to $6\frac{1}{2}$ tiles, 4 tiles cannot be correct.

> BECEUSE I MAGRD
>
> THE FISH ON TOP

Vic's Work

Partially Meeting the Benchmark

Some students may say, "No, Kim cannot be right" but offer no explanation. Ask these students to explain orally how they know to make sure that they realize that if the fish measures $6\frac{1}{2}$ tiles, it cannot also measure 4 tiles.

Not Meeting the Benchmark

Some students may say that Kim could be right even though they measured the fish to be a different length.

End-of-Unit Assessment

Problem 1

Benchmark addressed:

Benchmark 4: Understand that measuring with different-sized units will result in different numbers.

In order to meet the benchmark, students' work should show that they can:

- Explain different units of measure will lead to different measurements.

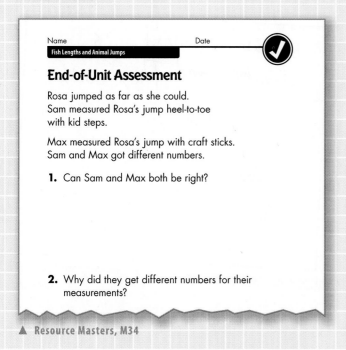

Name _____ Date _____

Fish Lengths and Animal Jumps

End-of-Unit Assessment

Rosa jumped as far as she could.
Sam measured Rosa's jump heel-to-toe
with kid steps.

Max measured Rosa's jump with craft sticks.
Sam and Max got different numbers.

1. Can Sam and Max both be right?

2. Why did they get different numbers for their measurements?

▲ **Resource Masters, M34**

Meeting the Benchmark

Students who meet the benchmark indicate that Sam and Max can both be right if they were measuring with different units.

Isabel wrote, "Because they were measuring with different things."

> because they were measureing with different things.

Isabel's Work

Chris specified that craft sticks are bigger than Jake's feet. In fact, we do not know whether Sam's feet are larger or smaller than the craft sticks. The important point is that Chris knows that the two units are different.

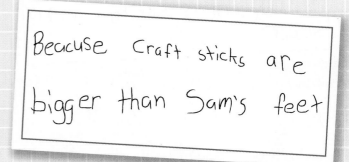

> Because Craft sticks are bigger than Sam's feet

Chris's Work

Carol said that kid steps are bigger than craft sticks. This response is correct for the same reason.

Carol's Work

Partially Meeting the Benchmark

Paul wrote, "The reason they are different is because one is bigger and one is smaller." There is no indication that the *units* (or tools, or things we measure with) are different sizes. Ask this student to explain his answer to see whether he identifies the *unit size* as what matters.

> The resen Tharare diffrent
> is BXUs wun is Bikr and wun is
> smolr

Paul's Work

Not Meeting the Benchmark

Even though Marta and Seth said that Sam and Max could both be right, their explanations indicate that they did not understand the question.

Marta's Work

Seth's Work

Measuring with Partial Units

Students have all measured a fish that is about $6\frac{1}{2}$ inches long and are discussing their findings. In this conversation, students are trying to describe measurements that result in partial units. Students have laid out 7 tiles, the last tile extending beyond the fish. The challenge is to name the amount this shows.

Teacher: Why did we want to measure the fish?

Paula: Because we want to know how long it is. Exactly.

Teacher: We want to find out *exactly* how long it is. Raise your hand to tell us how long your fish is.

Nicky: About 7.

Teacher: How many tiles are on your fish?

Nicky: 7.

Richard: 7 and a half.

Richard has made a common error. He sees the 7 tiles, the last tile extending beyond the fish, and included that last tile in his count. Then, recognizing that only part of the tile was on the fish, he added $\frac{1}{2}$ to his count—$7\frac{1}{2}$.

Teacher: How many *whole* tiles are on your fish? Take off any tile that is only partially on.

Richard [takes off the last tile and recounts]**:** A little more than 6.

Tuan: I used 7, but it was only 6 and a half.

Teacher: Why would you say 6 and a half?

Tuan: Because this is 6 and this right here is a half.

Teacher: Tuan is saying that 6 of the tiles are on the fish, but the last tile is only halfway on the fish. Raise your hand if yours is the same way.

The teacher notices that William has fit 6 tiles completely on the fish and part of a seventh tile.

Teacher: William, do you have 7 tiles all the way on the fish?

William: (Nodding.) You could say 7 and a half.

Tuan: But 7 and a half goes a little into 8.

Teacher: Count the tiles completely on your fish.

Neil: I would say 6 and a quarter.

Keena: It's in between.

Teacher: In between what? There have to be two numbers for it to be in between.

Keena: 6 and 7.

Teacher: It's not exactly 6 and it's not exactly 7, so it's in between 6 and 7. How should you record it?

Paul: 6 and one half.

Teacher: Who else likes to say it's 6 and a half tiles?

A few of the students raise their hands.

Teacher: Who says "in between 6 and 7"? Who says "a little more than 6"? . . . Who says "a little less than 7"? . . . These are all ways to describe the same length. They all describe how long this fish is. We can say "about 7," too, but it doesn't give as much information.

As children are learning to measure, there are several challenging ideas that they must put together. One is that even though they needed 7 tiles to completely cover the fish, the count can be identified as 6 and a half, or a little more than 6. It is difficult for them to see that the seventh tile is not included in the whole-number count. Students are also working on the idea that, if the measurement is done correctly using the same unit, they should all get the same result. However, there are a variety of ways to describe that same result.

Dialogue Box

Understanding Comparison Problems

The class has been working on comparison problems. When they were first given these kinds of problems, several students struggled to understand what was being asked. For example, the first problem on *Student Activity Book* page 11 is the following:

> Sam caught a perch that is 8 inches long.
>
> He caught an alewife that is 11 inches long.
>
> How much longer is the alewife than the perch?

As they began to solve the problem, some students laid out 11 tiles and 8 tiles and then found the total number of tiles. The teacher paid particular attention to these students, helping them picture the two fish to understand the question "How much longer is one than the other?"

Now students have come together to share their strategies for solving the problem about Sam's fish. But first the teacher wants to make sure that everyone understands what the problem is about. To help students think about it, the teacher has found a copy of a perch that is 8 inches long and a copy of an alewife that is 11 inches long.

Teacher: What do we know about this problem?

Bruce: The perch is 8 inches long.

The teacher asks Bruce to use the tiles to show how long the perch is. She lays down a picture of an 8-inch perch, and Bruce carefully lines up tiles flush against one another across the length of the picture, seeming to count as he lays each tile. As he lines up the tiles, the teacher asks the class whether there are any spaces in his line of tiles. When he finishes covering the fish, the class counts the tiles as he points to each one.

Teacher: What else do we know about this problem?

Bruce: The alewife is 11 inches tall.

The teacher holds up a picture of an 11-inch alewife and then lays it parallel to the perch with the mouths of the two fish adjacent.

Bruce lays out tiles the length of the alewife. The class counts the tiles as Bruce points to each one from 1 to 11.

Teacher: We know three things. We know that the perch is 8 inches and that the alewife is 11 inches. We also know that the alewife is longer than the perch. Here's what we don't know: how much longer is the alewife than the perch? How much does the perch need to grow to be as long as the alewife? Who can point to where we need to look?

Allie: You need to look at where the two fish are. (She points to the empty space after the 8-inch fish.)

Teacher: What did you find out?

Allie: For it to be 11, you have to count the space where it needs to be.

Teacher: How much longer does the perch need to grow? (3) Three what? (Inches)

Paul goes up and shows how he moved his finger from the tiles on the perch up to the tiles on the alewife to see that it needed 3 more.

Comparison problems are challenging for many first graders. In order to help her students picture what the problem was about, the teacher used pictures of two fish so that students could point to the difference in length between the alewife and the perch. Even though many of her students had solved the problem correctly, it was important for them to return to the problem to remember the context of the question.

More Measuring with Partial Units

Students may continue to struggle with partial units in the second investigation. In this session, as students measured tapes with craft sticks, baby steps, and basketball player steps, many of the teacher's conversations with students involved partial units.

When Danielle took 11 steps and had some tape left over, she took a 12th step and said that the distance was "between 12 and 13." Her partner, Edgar, said, "No, it's between 12 and 11."

Teacher: Let's think about this. Danielle said it's between 12 and 13, but Edgar said that that's not right. How are you thinking about it?

Edgar: She couldn't fit all of her 12th step on. She did 11 whole steps and a little more.

Danielle nods.

Teacher: So it's between 11 and 12.

The teacher turns to another pair.

Teacher: How long was Tape E?

Diego: About 9.

Teacher: Is there another way to say that?

Diego: 8 and a little bit.

The teacher observes Talisa as she measures a distance as $11\frac{1}{2}$ but calls it 12.

Teacher: How many whole craft sticks did you use?

Talisa: What does that mean?

Teacher: Did you use this whole stick (holds up the 12th stick) or did you just use a piece of it?

Talisa: Just a piece.

Teacher: I'm going to pull this off (removes the 12th stick) because you only used a piece of it. Now count how many whole sticks you used.

Talisa counts 11 sticks.

Teacher: You used 11 and a little bit of this one. You can record that as 11 and a little bit.

Felipe: Or she can write 11 and a half.

Turning to another pair, the teacher notices that Lyle and Sacha are measuring a distance that is not exactly 9 craft sticks. She encourages them to find a way to show that.

Lyle: Can you make a suggestion?

Teacher: What's a way to record measurements that are in between?

Sacha: Almost.

Teacher: How did Diego say it before?

Diego: About.

Teacher: You said a little bit more than 9. Could you say that it's in between 9 and 10?

Sacha and Diego: Yes!

Teacher: If you say *about,* I don't know if you mean a little more than 9 or less than 9. Be specific.

Using numbers to measure length is different from using numbers to count a discrete quantity. When students count objects, each successive counting number refers to one object. But to use numbers to measure length, students have to develop the sense of a continuous interval. If the measured length does not extend to the end of the last unit, then that last count, in a sense, does not count. Students must learn to think in terms of a length as *between* two whole units and then learn how to describe that. For some students, this may continue to be a challenge through the end of the investigation.

Dialogue Box

More Steps or Fewer?

In the previous session, students learned to measure distances with kid steps. They also measured various distances in the classroom and discussed which distances were longer than others. Today they meet to discuss the numbers—how many kid feet the distances are. They quickly see that different students got different counts for the same distance.

Teacher: Jacob found out that the length of the strip was 8 of his own feet. And look where he stopped walking, just about at the end of the tape. Let's try again with a different person. Will it be the same, also 8?

Leah: No, because people's feet are smaller.

Teacher: What about my foot?

Felipe: Lower.

Teacher: My foot would be smaller?

Felipe: No, bigger. It takes more space.

Teacher: So if I measure this line with my feet, it'll take how many steps?

Felipe: Like 7 or 6.

The teacher walks the strip, taking 6 steps.

Teacher: Now we're going to measure the length of the strip by using our hands. How could we do that?

Michelle: Just like with our feet. (She demonstrates.)

Teacher: Will it take more "steps" or fewer?

Leah: More, because your hand is smaller than your foot.

The teacher asks students to raise their hands if they agree with Leah. A few do, but many think it will take fewer steps, because a hand is smaller than a foot.

Teacher: How many of Bruce's hands do you think our tape will be?

Students make a few predictions and then count aloud as Bruce measures the tape strip with his hands. When he has finished, some students think the total is 14 and a half, and others call it 15 and a half.

Teacher: Let's try again. Remember to start with your hand right at the beginning of the tape.

Bruce repeats; when he takes the extra partial "step," the teacher says, "13 and a half."

Felipe: I thought it was 14.

Carol: I thought it was 15.

They watch Bruce one more time and agree that the number is more than 13 and less than 14. As they compare that with their predictions, they notice that the number of hands is more than the number of feet for the same length.

Teacher: Would it make a difference if I measured the length of the strip with my hands? (Most students say yes.) Why?

Toshi: Because your hands are different.

Teacher: How are they different?

Marta: They're bigger.

Teacher: How much bigger?

Felipe: A little bit. So it'd be like 10.

The teacher measures and finds that the length is a little bit more than 10 hands. Throughout this discussion, students have been involved in thinking about how to repeat a unit to measure a length and how different units give different counts for the same length.

Student Math Handbook

The *Student Math Handbook* pages related to this unit are pictured on the following pages. This book is designed to be used flexibly: as a resource for students doing classwork, as a book students can take home for reference while doing homework and playing math games with their families, and as a reference for families to better understand the work their children are doing in class.

When students take the *Student Math Handbook* home, they and their families can discuss these pages together to reinforce or enhance students' understanding of the mathematical concepts and games in this unit.

Measurement

Math Words
• measurement

Measurement can tell you how long, how heavy, or how tall a thing is, or how much space it takes up. You have already taken many measurements. Your height, your weight, and your shoe size are all different kinds of measurement.

We will practice measuring the lengths of objects and the lengths of distances. We will find out how long and how far different things are.

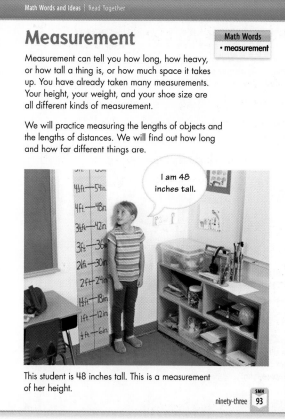

I am 48 inches tall.

This student is 48 inches tall. This is a measurement of her height.

ninety-three   SMH 93

◀ Math Words and Ideas, p. 93

Measuring Objects

Look around the room. There are many objects and they can all be measured. The measurements can be compared.

What is the longest object you see?
What is the shortest?
Are there any objects that are close in size?
How can you tell whether two objects are exactly the same size?

Measuring objects is important to make sure that things are the right size.

My shoe is longer than my baby brother's shoe.

SMH 94   ninety-four

◀ Math Words and Ideas, p. 94

Length

When you measure length, you measure the long part of an object.

If you are measuring carefully, you should get the same answer each time you measure the same length.

The length of this vase

The length of this book

The length of this desk

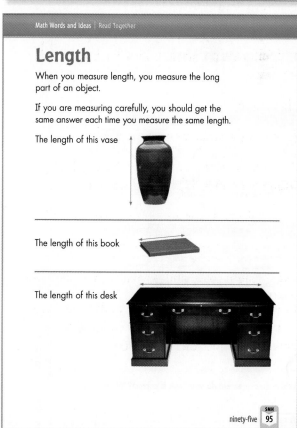

ninety-five   SMH 95

◀ Math Words and Ideas, p. 95

Unit

Math Words
• unit

A unit is what you use to measure. When you have finished measuring, count how many units you have used.

Units of paper clips:

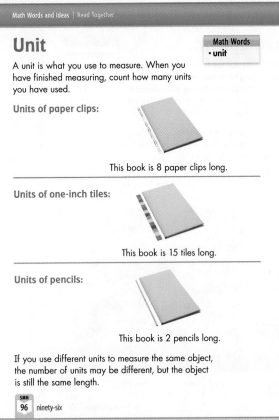

This book is 8 paper clips long.

Units of one-inch tiles:

This book is 15 tiles long.

Units of pencils:

This book is 2 pencils long.

If you use different units to measure the same object, the number of units may be different, but the object is still the same length.

SMH 96 ninety-six

◄ Math Words and Ideas, p. 96

Measuring with Units

(page 1 of 2)

If you measure carefully, you will get the same number each time you measure the same object. To measure carefully, make sure that the units line up in a straight line and touch at the edges.

Kira used paper clips to measure her pen. She kept getting different numbers.

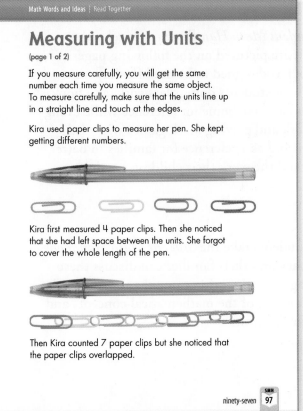

Kira first measured 4 paper clips. Then she noticed that she had left space between the units. She forgot to cover the whole length of the pen.

Then Kira counted 7 paper clips but she noticed that the paper clips overlapped.

ninety-seven **SMH 97**

◄ Math Words and Ideas, p. 97

Measuring with Units

(page 2 of 2)

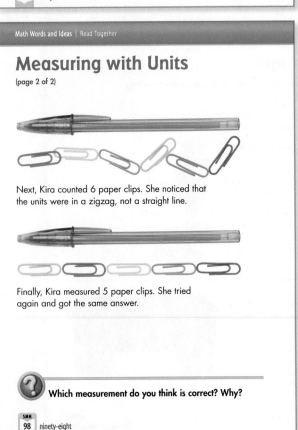

Next, Kira counted 6 paper clips. She noticed that the units were in a zigzag, not a straight line.

Finally, Kira measured 5 paper clips. She tried again and got the same answer.

? Which measurement do you think is correct? Why?

SMH 98 ninety-eight

◄ Math Words and Ideas, p. 98

Inch

Math Words
• inch

An inch is a unit that people can use to measure how long something is.

This line is one inch long. _____

There are many tools we can use to measure in inches.

This tile is 1 inch on each side:

This pencil is 5 inches long:

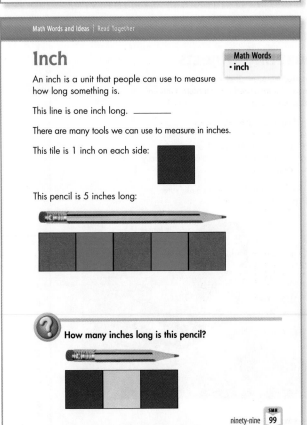

? How many inches long is this pencil?

ninety-nine **SMH 99**

◄ Math Words and Ideas, p. 99

Partial Units (page 1 of 2)

Sometimes when we measure an object, its length falls between two units. There are many ways to talk about this.

Some children measured this pencil with inch tiles.

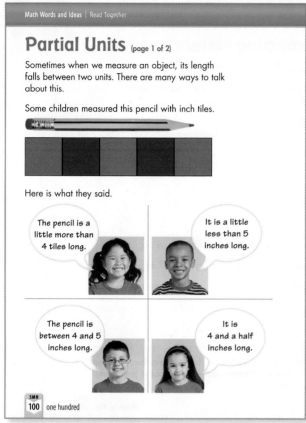

Here is what they said.

The pencil is a little more than 4 tiles long.

It is a little less than 5 inches long.

The pencil is between 4 and 5 inches long.

It is 4 and a half inches long.

Math Words and Ideas, p. 100

Partial Units (page 2 of 2)

All of these ways are right! If you want to talk about something exactly between two whole units you can say it is all of the full units and one half of the last one.

This is how mathematicians write one half: 1/2 $\frac{1}{2}$

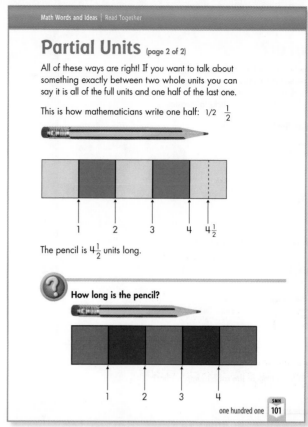

The pencil is $4\frac{1}{2}$ units long.

How long is the pencil?

Math Words and Ideas, p. 101

At Least

Math Words
• at least

At least means "as long as" or "longer than." For example, if you need a pencil that is at least 4 inches long, it can be 4, 5, 6, or more inches long.

These pencils are at least 4 inches long.

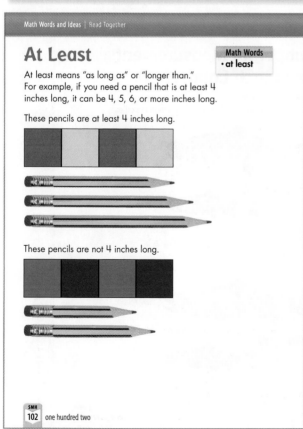

These pencils are not 4 inches long.

Math Words and Ideas, p. 102

Measuring Distances

Math Words
• distance

Distance is the length between one place and another.

Look at where you are sitting and the nearest door. There is a distance between you and the door. Think about your home and your school. This is a distance you travel every day.

How do you travel a short distance? Did you ever go very far away from home? How did you travel?

Measuring distance is important to find out how far away or close together things are.

Math Words and Ideas, p. 103

How Far?

Rosa wondered how far her pets could jump.
So she measured the distance that each could jump.
She marked where they started and where they
landed. Then she used craft sticks to measure.

Her frog jumped 10 craft sticks.

Her rabbit jumped 8 craft sticks.

Her grasshopper jumped $6\frac{1}{2}$ craft sticks.

Her mouse jumped 5 craft sticks.

? **Did the frog or the rabbit jump farther?**

SMH
104 one hundred four

▲ Math Words and Ideas, p. 104

Comparing Measurements: How Much Farther?

Now that Rosa knows how far all of her pets jump,
she can compare their jumps.

This distance shows how much farther the frog jumped.

The frog jumped 2 craft sticks farther than the rabbit.

? **How much farther did the frog jump than the mouse?
How much farther did the grasshopper jump than
the mouse?**

one hundred five **SMH**
105

▲ Math Words and Ideas, p. 105

Ordered Lists

Rosa organized the jumps in an ordered list from
longest to shortest.

The jump on the top of the list is the longest, or
farthest, distance.

The jump on the bottom of the list is the shortest
distance.

Animal Jumps

Longest	Frog	10 craft sticks
Next Longest	Rabbit	8 craft sticks
Next Longest	Grasshopper	$6\frac{1}{2}$ craft sticks
Shortest	Mouse	5 craft sticks

SMH
106 one hundred six

▲ Math Words and Ideas, p. 106

Comparing Measurements: How Much Longer?

To compare the lengths of these two fish, line up one
end and measure how much longer one is than the other.

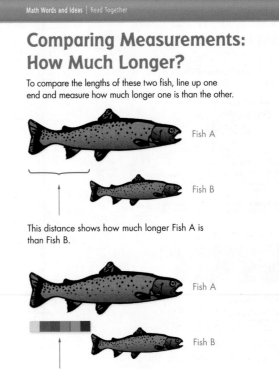

Fish A

Fish B

This distance shows how much longer Fish A is
than Fish B.

Fish A

Fish B

Fish A is 6 squares longer than Fish B.

one hundred seven **SMH**
107

▲ Math Words and Ideas, p.107

Index